CW00747044

Encouraging Innovation in the Eighteenth and Nineteenth Centuries

The Society of Arts and Patents 1754–1904

Fuelling an Industrial Revolution
(above) by canal barge to Manchester, circa 1780 *(Reproduced by kind permission of the Manchester Central Library Local Studies Unit.)*
(below) by steam-hauled wagon train to Leeds, circa 1814 *(Reproduced from George Walker's Costumes of Yorkshire (1814) by kind permission of the Kirklees Community History Service, Tolson Memorial Museum, West Yorkshire.)*
(The Duke of Bridgewater received a gold medal of the Society of Arts in recognition of the canal system that he developed. John Blenkinsop received a patent (1811) for 'mechanical means whereby the conveyance of coal and other articles is facilitated'.)

Encouraging Innovation in the Eighteenth and Nineteenth Centuries

The Society of Arts and Patents, 1754–1904

First Edition, 2006

James Harrison

High View, Gunnislake

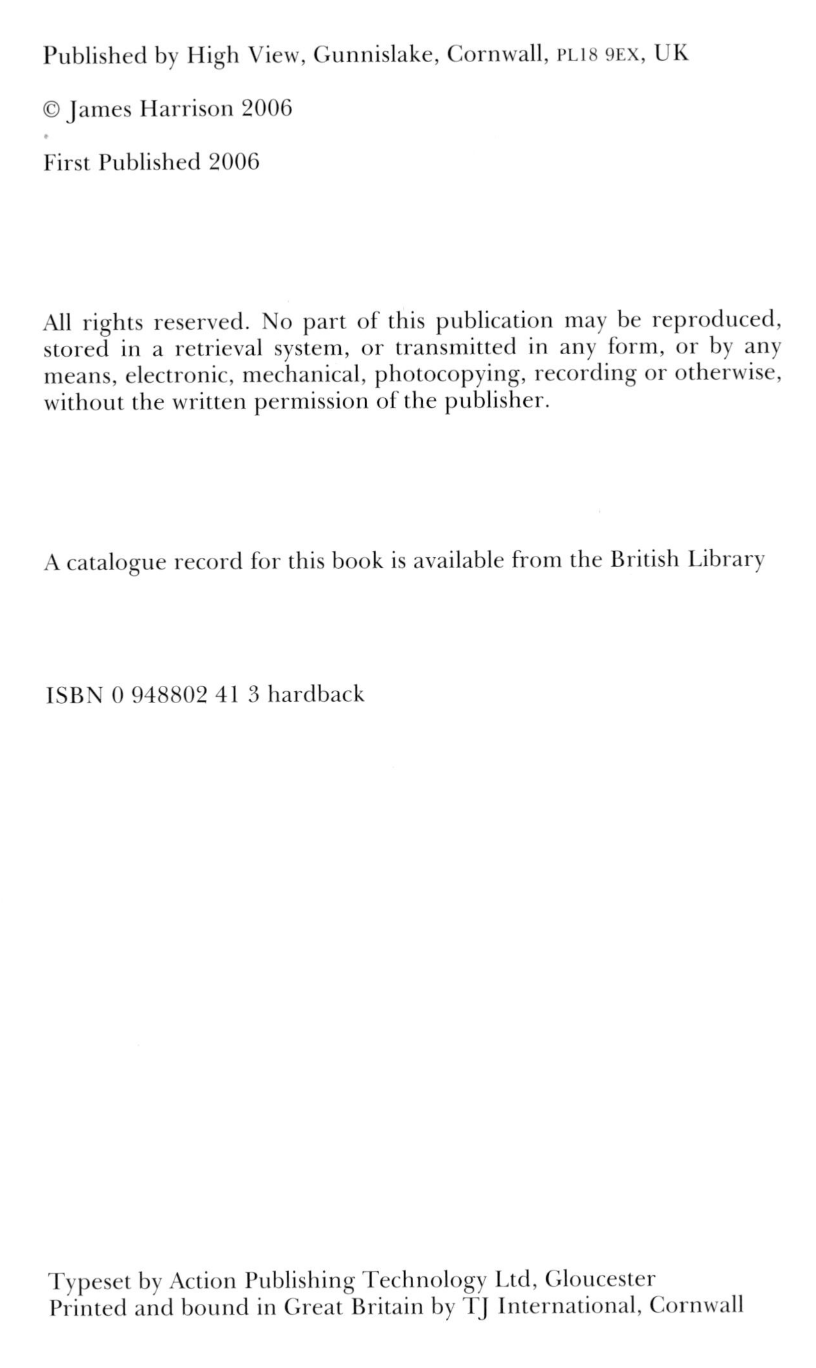

Published by High View, Gunnislake, Cornwall, PL18 9EX, UK

First Published 2006

A catalogue record for this book is available from the British Library

ISBN 0 948802 41 3 hardback

Typeset by Action Publishing Technology Ltd, Gloucester
Printed and bound in Great Britain by TJ International, Cornwall

Dedication

To my mother

whose infinite patience and care
during difficult times
encouraged a spirit of improvement in me

Statements of Aims and Objects

The Society of Arts

'The encouragement of Arts, Manufactures and Commerce in Great Britain, by bestowing Rewards, from Time to Time, for such Productions, Inventions, or Improvements, as shall tend to the employing of the Poor, to the Increase of Trade, and to the Riches and Honour of this Kingdom, by Promoting Industry and Emulation.' 1754

Patents

'We, being willing to give encouragement to all Arts and Inventions which may be for the Public Good, are graciously Pleased to condescend to his Request' [for the grant of a Monopoly limited to a specific subject for a restricted Period.] 1769

(Corresponding passages to this quotation from Letters Patent of George III to James Watt appeared in patents for inventions from Elizabeth I to Elizabeth II. Wording was altered from time to time, but not the purport.)

Contents

Illustrations

Introduction

During the closing weeks of 1945 the London Section of the Textile Institute held its first post-war meeting and, as a member new to London, I made a point of attending. The venue was a room bare of all but the furnishings necessary for such a gathering. I now know it as the Benjamin Franklin Room of the Royal Society of Arts' Adelphi House. After its restoration from war damage, I attended meetings in the Society's main lecture hall when it was made available to other organisations in which I had an interest. In this way my curiosity regarding the Society was aroused, and by the time of the Society's bicentenary in 1954 I had been accepted as a Fellow.

A fresh awareness of the richness of its history and archives arising from bicentennial events led the Society to appoint a curator/historian who, within a short time of taking office, started a History Study Group. Though not present at this Group's first meeting I was not far behind and from then began a friendship with the curator/historian – David Allan – from which I have derived great benefit. He soon suggested I offer a paper to the Group on 'The Society and Patents' – as later he was to invite others to relate areas of contact between their specialities and the Society. Publication in the Society's *Journal* of many of these later contributions has added immensely to the record of the Society's story. For a variety of reasons my early and tentative dissertations were not published but, stirred by a reminder of the 150th anniversary of the 1852 Patent Law Amendment Act, there seemed merit in expressing in print a more mature consideration of the subject to which David Allan had drawn my attention so long ago and encouraged me to pursue. While some of my obligations to him are specifically acknowledged in the following pages his influence permeates the whole.

Some eighteen months or so prior to the Society's celebration of a double century, the Patent Office scored its first hundred. It did so quietly with the publication of a booklet – *Patent Office Centenary* – researched by a member of its staff, Herbert Harding. Although Harding had entered the Office forty years before me, neither seniority in years nor rank prevented him from offering friendship and guidance until I entered into his legacy as informal Patent Office historian. He also is referred to specifically in the following pages but my debt to him is greater than the few attributions would indicate.

Alan Gomme, a contemporary of Harding, I only met briefly; he also prepared a booklet – *Patents of Invention; Origin and Growth of the Patent System in Britain* – published by the British Council in 1946. Gomme had been head of the Patent Office Library for many years in succession to Wyndham Hulme whose essays some forty to fifty years earlier in the *Law Quarterly Review* on the development of patent law and practice are scholarly exercises that can still be relied on as providing sound information. About the same time William Martin, Chief Examiner of Patents, published a little gem – *The English Patent System.*

Apart from the officially produced *Reports of Patent Cases* and a handful of privately-compiled patent law reports issued earlier, the brief publications of Harding, Gomme, Hulme and Martin provided, with few exceptions, the principal literature on the history of the patent system over a considerable period. A wider interest in the subject has been evident during the last thirty or forty years; of these more recent studies I have made most use for the present paper of that painstakingly researched by Harry Dutton, one-time lecturer in Economic History at the University of Lancaster. I had the pleasure of meeting him and readily acknowledge that his work has provided me with much information. His treatise – *The Patent System and Inventive Activity during the Industrial Revolution, 1750–1852* – was published in 1984.

That economic historians have fairly recently 'discovered' patents and have sought to assess their significance during the period chosen by Dutton I have found fascinating. Lacking formal history training and with no grounding whatever in economic history, I observe with respectful astonishment attempts to chart significant cause and effect relationships between patents and industrial growth prior to reform of the patent system. (I have noticed also that Jewkes and others seem to have had difficulty assessing the effect of patents on twentieth century economic growth even after some degree of reform of patent procedures had taken place – see *The Sources of Invention*, 1958).

Prior to 1852 patents were costly in money and time to acquire and of uncertain value when obtained; both before and after grant they were open to challenge in courts antipathetic to any form of monopoly. For these and other reasons patent grants were relatively few in the eighteenth century. A handful of them stand out as highly beneficial to their proprietors and no doubt these provided a stimulus to others to seek profit by innovation, but on the whole I find it difficult to accept that the patent system affected significantly the pattern of industrial development during the first half-century of the Society of Arts.

Although, doubtless, patents had **some** effect in promoting economic growth prior to the nineteenth century their influence can be over-stated. On the other hand, the manner in which some writers dismiss the activities of the Society of Arts during its early years as of little or no consequence is quite unacceptable. How many or how few of the Society's projects taken individually were or were not successful is secondary, what matter are the overall consequences of the Society's efforts to stimulate and sustain a climate responsive to change. The primary issue is whether the Society of Arts played a significant part in nurturing a 'Spirit of Improvement'. The right answer cannot be arrived at by being blinkered to observation of major innovations only. Small innovations matter. Small improvements may lead to important advances:- choice of the right leather to cover the drawing rollers of Arkwright's spinning machines was critical; without suitable dyestuffs specific for their purposes nylon and other synthetic fibres would have had limited uses; a skirt of suitable balance between rigidity and flexibility with adequate tear-resistance and linear strength had to be developed if the hovercraft was not to be limited to use in calm waters. The success of a major innovation is not infrequently dependent on the solution of subsidiary problems.

Innovation is brought about gradually. Seldom is there a major progressive step without antecedent activity, often over a long period and frequently involving people who 'failed' but in 'failing' provided elements of information useful to eventual success. Innovation is rarely a consequence of one person's lone effort and it generally arises in response to need – need to improve productivity, to reduce prices, to eliminate a bottleneck restricting growth, to expedite movement of products, and so on. So it was in or about the year of the Society's foundation when a group of Lancashire mine-owners proposed to have a stream giving access to the Mersey made navigable in order to facilitate transport of their coal. There was nothing new in improving small rivers to ease the passage of boats; it had been done for centuries. Over the years methods and riparian appliances had been devised and modified so that even narrow and/or shallow streams could be put to use. In the event, the Sankey Brook was a stream too far, for by the time its bends had been straightened and its gradients stepped it was more canal than river – and is now regarded as the first canal in England of modern times. A few miles away another coalmine proprietor took note and entered on a more ambitious project and, following the success of this venture – the Bridgewater canal – canal mania was soon under way.*

At the same time as the Sankey canal was being undertaken in Lancashire, a mine-owner in Yorkshire was having a waggonway (i.e. a railway) constructed to carry coal from his Middleton pits to the nearby navigable river and to the town of Leeds. Half a century later his wooden rails were replaced by iron – by then more readily available. These were strong

* The mine-owners who had turned the Sankey Brook into a canal were not content with one major innovation only. In 1793 trials of a steamboat were made on their canal. The Duke of Bridgewater was not to be outdone and in 1797 a steamboat travelled along his canal from Runcorn to Manchester. (This was three years earlier than the more celebrated Charlotte Dundas' trials on the Firth-Clyde Canal.) – Hatfield and Biddle, *The Canals of North West England*, 1970, Vol.1, p.93.

enough to support a steam locomotive thereby permitting greater loads to be hauled in one train. Additional to the commercial pressures of supplying coal at competitive prices, the carnage of conflict and the advanced cost of horse-fodder served to accelerate the development of steam haulage and the railway era began with coal deliveries. By 1812 when the Blenkinsop locomotive first moved erratically from the Middleton mines to Leeds, waggonways had been known for hundreds of years, Newcomen-type steam engines had been employed at collieries for nearly a century, for at least seventy years coke-smelted iron had been produced in increasing quantities at decreasing prices, improved steam engines transmitting rotative – as distinct from linear-power only – had made possible steam-powered wheeled vehicles forty years before Blenkinsop put his locomotive on rails (preceded let it be said by Trevithick, who assisted the construction of the Blenkinsop locomotives by not allowing his patent to be an impediment) and so, element by element, the components of the steam-railway were ready to be brought together to meet desirable ends, that is, to provide higher through-put, reduce transport costs and lessen the risks of bottlenecks in delivery of goods to consumers arising from war-time shortages of horses and horse-fodder.*

Canal systems and railways illustrate the evolutionary character of technological change; a step by step transition with

* 'When it is considered that this invention is applicable to all rail-roads, and that upon the works of Mr. Brandling [colliery-owner] alone, the use of 50 horses will be dispensed with, and the corn necessary for the consumption of, at least 200 men saved, we cannot forbear to hail the invention as of vast public utility, and to rank the inventor amongst the benefactors of his country' – *Leeds Mercury*, 27 June, 1812. The instant success of the Blenkinsop locomotives led to one being put to colliery use in Wigan eight months later. Another went to Newcastle and attracted the attention of George Stephenson. By coincidence discussions relating to the creation of the Society of Arts, the Sankey Brook navigation and the Middleton waggonway were taking place at approximately the same time. The first meeting of the Society of Arts occurred in 1754, the Sankey canal opened in 1757 and the Act authorizing the Middleton waggonway (regarded by some as the first British Railway Act) passed in 1758.

fresh needs being met as they arose. A competitive society has its own built-in stimuli and industrial development would have progressed steadily through the eighteenth and much (if not all) of the nineteenth without a patent system or a Society of Arts – which is not to say that neither made a useful contribution.

In the latter half of the nineteenth century when abolition of the patent system was being vigorously debated it was argued that since inventions are created by need and there is always knowledge available to meet the need, the need will always be met and, likely enough, by more than one person; as the knowledge was there for all to use, the step of matching knowledge to need does not merit reward. It is a persuasive argument, especially for a manufacturer who prefers not to pay for the skill or initiative required to perform the mental bridge-building exercise required to span the gap between the known and the as yet unknown and the attendant persistence necessary to reduce idea to practice even when one attempt after another fails to achieve the desired object.

A curious aspect of the fulfilling of industrial needs is that while the need may be obvious to many, few attempt to make good that which is lacking. No less curious is that a surprising number of those who venture on the attempt are outsiders to the branch of trade involved. While twentieth century examples of this phenomenon may be cited, they were much more common in the eighteenth. A few illustrations from that and the early nineteenth century will be sufficient to illustrate the point:

For more than a century smelting iron with coal had been seen as increasingly desirable but it was not until a maker of brass 'bellied pots' (three-legged cauldrons), recalling information gleaned from the malting industry to which he had been apprenticed, made the essential breakthrough. The manufacture of sulphuric acid in commercial quantities was introduced by a quack doctor. A shroud-maker conceived the machines used in the world's first power cotton spinning factory. According to a report recorded in the *Transactions of the Society of Arts* a drawback of these spinning machines was the delicacy of the works 'equal almost to that of clocks' but even before that report was printed a clock-maker of Warrington was working on improvements. An itinerant barber and wig-maker brought these and other improvements from other sources together to put spinning by power on a sound basis. A scientific instrument-maker prompted by a professor of chemistry is credited with the greatest eighteenth century improvements to the steam engine; later, urged on by a Birmingham 'toy-man', he rendered the steam engine capable of providing rotative power. A country parson devised the first clumsy power loom and then invented the earliest successful wool-combing machine. A lad sent to learn silk-weaving north of Manchester fascinated by the attempts of a rope-manufacturer to propel a boat on a local canal without the aid of horses was later to share with a Hendon farmer (who had worked independently) a government award for practical contributions to the screw-propulsion of ships.

The reasons why problems well-known in an industry are not always solved by personnel involved in it are numerous and varied, but of no immediate interest. That it is so – and was all the more so in the eighteenth century – is more pertinent to the present topic because it points to the desirability of there being as wide an awareness of needs as possible and of there being facilities for dissemination and sharing of ideas regarding possible solutions. It is perhaps here that the Society of Arts' greatest contribution to industrial change during its first hundred years is to be found. Its Premium Lists were inventories of needs very real in their times. They were not compiled by a dilettante group of do-gooders – as can too readily be assumed – but by people of standing in a variety of spheres, people with their feet firmly on the ground and who were able, when lacking specific technical information, to call upon acquaintances prepared to provide advice and, where advantageous to the Society, practical assistance.

During the eighteenth century philosophical or scientific societies for the exchange of knowledge were formed in many towns. The Society of Arts had totally different objectives from substantially all of those but in a period before the establishment of specialist professional bodies dealing with such subjects as fell within the business of the Society's Committees – more particularly those of Agriculture, Chemistry, Manufactures and Mechanics – the Society provided a meeting ground for like minds and for the sharing of news, information and ideas. It may well be that the widest ranging discussions took place next door to the Society's house in the Adelphi Tavern or at some other congenial venue; no matter if much consideration of current issues took place extramurally, the Society made it possible. Almost all the people attending meetings of the Committee of Mechanics in the Society's earliest years, for example, were practising civil engineers whose names are still recalled with respect by their professional successors. They were ready to consult with others of their kind not in membership when additional opinions seemed desirable – men such as John Smeaton, perhaps the most celebrated of eighteenth century engineers. In similar manner, the Committee of Chemistry had its own competent elected members but they had contact with non-members who were drawn in to perform services to the Society, men such as William Lewis and his colleague Alexander Chisholm who did much to promote the coalescence of chemistry and industry and who were always ready to be of assistance to the Society. Turning to another important branch of industry – iron working; John Wilkinson, one of Britain's foremost iron-masters, and John Cockshutt, London representative of a family business possessing forges at Rotherham and Sheffield, both took an active part at the Society in matters relating to their industry following their elections to membership at the proposal of Samuel More. The Wilkinson and Cockshutt forges were among several visited and their ores and processes carefully noted by More's close acquaintances Lewis and Chisholm who shared information with him. In addition to its active membership, through More* (for thirty years its Secretary) the Society had an astonishing country-wide network of contacts with fingers on the pulses of many industries.

In retrospect the 'needs' to which the Society drew attention

* A former Secretary to the Society has paid tribute to the remarkable breadth of More's mind and interests and referred to his travels to make or renew acquaintances in a wide range of industries to observe practical developments in forges, works and factories – G. E. Mercer 'Mr. More of the Adelphi', *RSA Jnl.*, Vol.127 (1979), pp.96–103, 173–179, 237–244.

in its Premium Lists may seem secondary when not inconsequential. However, as mentioned earlier, the importance of the secondary ought not to be under-estimated. This point is well shown in the first brief list of subjects selected for encouragement by the founding fathers; it included domestic production of the madder plant, the ground-up roots of which had been employed as a colouring agent for fabrics and leather from early times. Without adequate supplies of this commodity the burgeoning cotton industry (where output had risen by approximately fifty per cent in the quarter century to 1754) could have been restricted. Even greater and more prolonged efforts were later made by the Society to expedite the introduction of the Turkey-red process. The secret of this method of dyeing had been obtained by the French, and the Dutch also had acquired the know-how; it was vital, therefore, that the UK should master the process. Again in a competitive climate – in this case within an international high pressure area – people involved in the branch of manufacture affected would eventually have found means of solving the problem (as indeed they did*) but in drawing general attention to the issue the Society served to sharpen minds, generate discussion and heighten awareness of a national need. Britain was gaining advantages over foreign competitors in mechanical aspects of cotton cloth production but fabric taken directly from the loom is uninteresting material. When dyed or printed, especially in colours as bright as Turkey-red, it takes on a totally different and far more attractive appearance. By drawing attention to what could have been a weakness, that is, an inability to match other countries in satisfactorily applying the brightest and fastest colours available to the products of the industry that was to

* John Wilson of Manchester, sent a man to live among the dyers of Smyrna and eventually acquired the secret process. (Madder was the essential colouring agent, the secret lay in the method of treating the fabric with various chemical agents.) Wilson received a Premium of £50 from the Society in 1761. Another leading dyer and printer, Dr. Charles Taylor (later to become Secretary to the Society), prevailed upon a Greek to take up residence in Manchester in order to operate the process in Taylor's works. Later, in 1786, two Frenchmen received a UK government grant of £2,500 for having communicated their method of dyeing Turkey-red.

become the country's greatest export earner, the Society showed itself to be well aware of a need of the time. What it was drawing attention to was secondary – but it mattered.

Secondary developments are rarely mentioned in history-books though they often make the difference between modest and greater success, as the replacement of glass vessels by lead-lined vats in sulphuric acid production or the Gilchrist-Thomas lining to the Bessemer convertor in steel manufacture. They may also avoid serious hold-ups in the development of major innovations – as could have been caused by the so-called 'elastic memory' of early nylon yarns resulting in such severe shrinkage problems following processing into cloth and/or garments as would make the latter unsaleable, or when, in the early 1920s, commercial exploitation of cellulose acetate fibres (long known to the public by the registered Trade Mark 'Celanese') was held back for lack of means to colour them satisfactorily until dyes specific to that compound were introduced. For all their failure to hit the headlines the secondary developments that help major innovations forward cannot be dismissed as inconsequential. If, after the lapse of years and advances in technology, many of the Society's eighteenth century projects now appear to be of little significance they may not have been so trivial in their time.

Whether the Society's method of encouragement by awards with its accompanying specialist committees deliberating on matters relevant to the needs of the time or the system of granting brief temporary monopolies by patent most assisted the flow of technical knowledge and stimulated industrial development in the eighteenth century is not assessed in the following essay which sets out merely to record some of the ways in which two different approaches to the quickening of innovation were pursued and how, towards the end of the Society's first century, both institutions underwent radical change each affecting the other.

At the Society change took place remarkably quickly as it moved from years of decline to a period of fresh vigour. This was a chapter in its history deserving closer study than is appropriate here. However the final section of this essay – which may appear chronologically out of position but which relates to this episode and is secondary to the principal narrative – concludes with a conjectural observation on why events took the course they did. Behind that speculation lie questions relating to the influence a long succession of technically-minded people might bring to bear on the Society if professional concerns were likely to be affected. Seeing that the old order was changing, did some of these people effect a coup or was the change from decline to renascent activity as straight forward as hitherto accepted? Whatever the explanation, account must be taken of the fact that the Society's membership doubled in the ten years following its 1840s constitutional reforms, with a disproportionately larger number of engineers and other technically-minded people among the new members. As previously indicated, those who gathered together in the Society's technical committees served the Society well but also gained advantage from the provision of a venue at which to share ideas and sharpen minds with others engaged in similar occupations. They had a beneficial interest in keeping the Society alive and operating in a manner suiting their professional concerns. As time went by and specialist professional institutions were established many of those who had gathered at the Society's house became core members of some of these organisations, but until those bodies were up and running the Society was important to them. Whatever merit there may be in this argument, the facts beyond question are that a great many of those who led the way in making Britain the 'Workshop of the World' found the Society a useful discussion ground for technical matters and consequently would have been sorry to lose such a facility.

Unlike the Society patents were not in decline in 1840 – rather the reverse. But long overdue changes in the system by which patents were granted had failed to materialise notwithstanding more than half a century of agitation for reform. However, many of the people who were keen to instil new life into the Society of Arts also had an interest in the improvement of the patent system. In the light of this, it was no coincidence that the Patent Law Amendment Act of 1852 – the first Act to alter materially the manner in which patent petitions were to be processed – was sometimes referred to as 'The Society of Arts' Act'.

It was a suggestion at the RSA that a recognition of the 150th

anniversary of the 1852 Patent Act might be appropriate that stimulated this much delayed essay in which information accumulated over many years has been brought together. Some of the source material is set out in a group of appendices. In addition, an article is annexed which was prepared for the Society's former 'Studies in the History and Archives' series and published in its *Journal*. Although it includes some repetitive material it also contains detailed information relative to the principal essay.

Acknowledgements

In addition to acknowledgements made specifically, both in the foregoing and in the pages following, there have been many who in a variety of ways have been helpful and to whom I am grateful. For example, there were the people who encouraged me to get writing when I felt I could not be bothered to take up themes long abandoned. And once the challenge was accepted there have been many who have provided more direct assistance. Of these I have in mind more particularly my late wife who displayed great tolerance as her husband pursued interests of little concern to her and who, notwithstanding, was called upon repeatedly to provide assistance; my friend and former colleague Dr. Raymond Smith, a fellow-member of the Newcomen Society whose conversation is always a delight and whose suggestions are invariably worth heeding; and Mrs. Susan Bennett one-time librarian/archivist and later curator at the RSA who was always ready – more especially when I could no longer easily visit the Society's House – to provide information and check facts with a cheerful spirit. (In addition, Mrs Bennett has rendered invaluable assistance in the preparation for publication of the final composition.) It is a long time since I pestered the staff of the Patent Office Library (as it then was) for material buried deep in nether regions but I was always kindly received and remain grateful. Exchanges of information with a former member of that staff, Mr. John Hewish, continue and to him I owe much. Science Museum staff were also helpful to me. Once the essay began to take shape Mrs. Margaret McClay worked wonders with her word processor interpreting handwriting not always of the clearest and too often obscured by revisions and corrections, and Mrs. Brenda Chopping, formerly of the Patent Office Examining Staff, has been generous of her time in reading the typescript and suggesting amendments.

1

'Greatest of all Rewards ... the pleasure of having done something for the benefit of Mankind'

'During a period of our social history when protection and monopoly were held ... to be the very tap roots of commercial prosperity and manufacturing industry, the Society of Arts discountenanced patents and monopolies of every kind.'

Chairman of Council of the Society of Arts, 1855[1]

There was an apparent dichotomy in the Society of Arts' attitude to patents throughout the greater part of its first century. From its early days public pronouncements were made which seemed increasingly to indicate an antipathy to patents notwithstanding a membership that included many in possession of patents and officers (both stipendiary and voluntary) who were active in giving advice and assistance to prospective and enrolled patentees.[2] This seemingly anomalous situation probably arose, at least in part, from the closeness of the objectives of the patent system and of the Society of Arts, resulting in intrusions of patent interests into the award-offering activities of the Society during its early years.

As originally envisaged the Society was to establish a fund from which pecuniary grants were to be made with the object of stimulating practical initiatives. Others had advocated the giving of premiums to encourage active skills and manufactures but with limited success until William Shipley persevered with a plan he had conceived and brought together a group of people prepared to give practical support to his scheme and to work towards its fulfilment.[3] At their first formal meeting in March 1754 eleven supporters of the scheme discussed the feasibility of offering financial inducements to encourage the domestic production of the raw materials of two important colouring agents imported at great cost – cobalt and madder. Industrial design also appears to have been in their minds for they additionally discussed prizes for drawings to be submitted by young people.[4] At the second meeting amounts of money to be offered as premiums were settled and arrangements set in train for press notices to be issued.

Neither investigations to seek out fresh sources of cobalt nor schemes to increase the acreage devoted to madder production were patentable and therefore no conflict with the patent system could arise. Further premium offers published in 1755 for the preparation of buff leather and the tinning of domestic vessels could have provided patentable subject-matter but no problems developed on these either. However, discussions early in 1756 relating to encouraging native production of saltpetre were interrupted when it was drawn to the Society's attention that a patent had recently been granted which claimed to disclose a method of making the substance. As the grant was found to be restricted to manufacture from vegetable sources only, the Society was able to proceed with its award offer by adding a warning in its advertisements to the effect that methods of production devised to meet its criteria had to be different from what was described in the specified patent.

There is a curious coincidence of timing associated with this patent. Dependence on imports of saltpetre (an essential ingredient of gunpowder) had been a cause for serious national concern over more than two centuries.[5] It was a matter that may well have been discussed among members and their acquaintances from the Society's earliest days. It was, however, an issue presenting great difficulties in promotion. Certainly a measure of ingenuity would be required to succeed in producing the material in quantity when so many other attempts had failed but, in addition, a major stumbling block lay in the necessity to set aside for a prolonged period – many years – an extensive parcel of land devoted solely to the development of this commodity. If the desired object could be achieved only by someone of considerable means, would an award of £50, or even £100, generate the desired interest?

Discussions on the merits of promoting a saltpetre premium were doubtless extensive and vigorous during 1754–5, and it is also reasonable to assume that opinions were sought outside the small promoting group. Was it coincidence then that a patent application was filed early in 1755, to be followed a few weeks later (as the practice was) by a description of an alleged method of production?[6] Be that as it may it was not long after the saltpetre episode that it became manifest that the Society's premium lists were emboldening inventive minds to seek out paths to the offices of the patent clerks.

During the spring of 1761 when the Society was giving thought to another year's premium list, including whether its offer of an award for isinglass (fish glue) should be continued, it was informed that a patent for making this substance was in force. It had been granted after the Society's first discussions of an award for the material. As anyone providing a method of preparing isinglass in order to obtain an award of the Society would be likely to infringe the patent and, however useful to the community that applicant's process may have been, the patent would prevent its use without the patentee's consent. Accordingly the Society discontinued its offer of awards for this subject. Arising from this interference with its objectives, the Society appointed a large special committee of men of standing to mull over the consequences of this patentee's intervention. The same patentee later took out two further patents related to subjects for which the Society was offering premiums. Meanwhile, advertisement of an award for crucibles resulted in an applicant successful before the Society following up his achievement by taking out a patent. For a few years, the number of people accepting awards of the Society and then taking out patents to cover the subject of the award increased.[7] This was a practice that in no way accorded with the Society's intentions.

In some measure the two schemes of stimulating innovation by awards were complementary: In its 1755 *Plan* the Society's object was given as 'the Encouragement of Arts, Manufactures and Commerce by bestowing Premiums for such productions Inventions or Improvements as shall tend to the employing of the Poor and the Increase of Trade'; while its first book of Rules and Orders (1758) opened with, 'When every Country in Europe is Attempting Manufactures; and Straining to gain a Superiority in Commerce; it must be the Desire of every Well

Wisher of his Country, to excite a Spirit of Emulation, to Encourage and Reward Ingenuity'. Though of more limited scope, the objective in granting patents for inventions was similar. The preamble to the grant document took a form varying little through the eighteenth century, 'We, being willing to give encouragement to all arts and inventions which may be for the publick use and benefit ...' Complementary the two award schemes may have been but that did not preclude the Society from being troubled over many years by reason of the very different natures of the awards obtainable under them.

Late in 1758 the Society gave consideration to a letter in which, *inter alia*, the writer mentioned that he was in possession of an invention for which he proposed to take out a patent. The Society was unequivocal in its response; 'it is contrary to the Institution and Design of the Society to encourage the obtaining of Patents'.[8] There was no suggestion of 'take out a patent if you like but do not expect additional encouragement from us', but rather that patents did not meet with the Society's approbation.

Perhaps it ought not to occasion surprise if patents did not find favour with the Society's founding fathers. In the two centuries since the royal prerogative had been brought into regular use as an instrument to encourage the development of industries new to the country, patents had had a chequered history resulting in their desirability being questioned. They involved the grant of a monopoly to the patentee for a term of years in which he had sole right to use the innovation. Under the Society's scheme the public had immediate access and freedom to use the objects of its awards.

The 1755 *Plan* of the Society which had set out its object as 'bestowing Premiums for such Productions, Inventions, or Improvements, as shall tend to the employing of the Poor and the Increase of Trade', was drawn up by Shipley's friend and founder member of the Society, Henry Baker, FRS.[9] Baker shared the philosophical interest and philanthropic concerns of another significant founder member, the Rev. Dr. Stephen Hales, FRS, perhaps the greatest scientist of his time.[10] All three, Shipley, Baker and Hales, were men of ideas from whom in a later generation patent applications may have been expected but none was made by them. Hales' system of ventilation of hospitals, gaols, ships and other confined spaces preserved innumerable lives and was a source of great satisfaction to him: 'I thank God, Ventilators in Ships, and Air Trunks in Gaols and Hospitals etc. prove Salutary beyond my most sanguine expectations ... I desire no other Reward, than that greatest of all Rewards, which I enjoy, viz: the pleasure of having done something for the benefit of Mankind'.[11]

Hales' sentiments were not uncommon in his time and for long afterwards. A contemporary, Abraham Darby, who achieved the important breakthrough of smelting iron with coal declined to patent a discovery which was so manifestly for the public good. Hales' life also overlapped in part that of Denis Papin FRS, a man of very inventive mind who was probably the first to exhibit the power of steam to move a piston in a cylinder; he was ideologically opposed to patenting anything he invented.[12] Opposition to patents on ideological grounds may have made the early Society's approach to encouraging innovation attractive to some subscribers.

On the other hand, there were people of high ideals in the Society who were in no way opposed to patents. Dr. Samuel Johnson who gave much time and thought to the Society (he was Chairman of at least one technical committee) is known to have offered unstinted support to a patentee's efforts to exploit his grant. There was, of course, more to Johnson than a *litterateur*, he was acutely aware of the tensions, strains and rivalries involved in commercial enterprises.[13] Manufacturers striving to keep their heads above water amid the hazards of competitive industries were not prominent in the Society in its early days.

In addition to ideological opposition to patents, Denis Papin had good grounds for a practical objection to the patent system he knew. This was to do with its failure to provide early disclosure of any invention the subject of a grant. The most common period during which the proprietors of a patent held a monopoly on the use of the discovery to which they laid claim was fourteen years but by secret working or official extension of the initial term of the original grant the period during which the discovery lay outside the public domain could be great, often inhibiting improvements. It was no doubt to Papin's chagrin that Thomas Savery's steam pump patent had an extended life span totalling thirty-five years.

It is against the background not only of the normal term of a patent monopoly being fourteen years but also of the not infrequent failure of patentees, by various means, to make their innovations available for general public exploitation even after the official period that the significance of the Society of Arts' requirement of immediate disclosure following an award should be seen.

A further inadequacy of the patent system of the time lay in the lack of examination of the practicability and novelty of alleged inventions. The Society of Arts on the other hand had developed careful procedures for checking the performance (and, where reasonably possible, originality) of subjects for which awards were claimed. This sometimes created two-fold trials for applicants: 'The great deliberation that most Venerable Society ... took in Writing made me dispair of receiving any Encouragement and therefore I Broke the Model with a resolution to bury it as thinking that Divine providence had not appointed me for the Ushering in of so Usefull an invention' was the forlorn complaint of one applicant. It was once observed from the Bench that it is common for inventors to see their inspired discoveries as the greatest boons to be bestowed upon mankind since Prometheus brought the fire of the Immortals down to mortal men, and the impatience of some of the Society's less sophisticated applicants is understandable. Another philosophical aspirant early abandoned hope: 'I have entertained the most Sanguine hopes that Curiosity would have Induced some of the worthy members of y^r Society to have sent me an ans^r for an Explanation. But I find the hopes of Man is vain, like the fleeting Joys of this transitory World that passes away and is no more seen'.[14]

There was an inevitable measure of delay when a project had first to be laid before a general meeting of members then referred to a committee for consideration, followed by further discussion at a general meeting consequential on the committee's report, sometimes resulting in a referral back to the committee. Notwithstanding such procedural delays, the assiduity with which members in general or in committee approached their voluntary tasks was commendable. Many

Artist's Impressions of two Society of Arts' Tests
(above) Model Ships (1762), *(below)* Seed Drill (1766)
(Reproduced by kind permission of the RSA)

matters on which they deliberated could not be handled quickly; experts had to be consulted, tests devised and carried out, or apparatus for checking performance prepared; for example, chemical analysis was required to ascertain the nature and purity of borax samples, physical tests were needed to check the quality of crucibles, the suitability of retorts for distilling acids could only be determined by repeated experimentation, the colour fastness of dyed yarns necessitated prolonged exposure to a variety of conditions, agricultural devices were frequently subjected to field trials, and there were instances where specialist equipment had to be improvised. And so on for the hundreds of subjects for which the Society offered awards.

Subject assessment was costly in time and money to the Society. It could also be costly for applicants. After periods of experimentation a model or a full-sized machine had to be made if the subject were mechanical, while samples of specified weight or form had to be prepared in the case of chemical products, such as saltpetre, borax, varnish or wood preservatives. When an applicant wrote of the problem of taking his 'test piece' to London from Sunderland – 'as he is unwilling to undertake so great a Journey and be disappointed therein ... [he] will be ready to bring up his Models, provided he has Encouragement' – he was answered kindly but firmly: 'If he designs to be a Candidate he must bring or send his Models by the Time that is limited, and if his Models have superior Merit, he will not fail of success'.[15]

Another out-of-town applicant gave the Society cause for thought within months of its foundation. (Had his approach been made a few years later when the Society had access to a wider range of 'judges' and was more accustomed to granting one-off awards ('bounties') to encourage improvements not specified in its premium lists he might have received greater satisfaction); 'A Brickmaker from Wimple in Cambridgeshire, being come to London on purpose to lay before the Society the Model of a Machine for the better and more expeditions manufacturing of Bricks & Tiles; after some Consideration and Debate, the Society ordered him to come in; and finding that he had Expectation of an immediate Reward they inform'd him, that according to their Plan they would not give Money for Machines whose real utility had not been tryed & properly recommended by Experienced Judges; that it would be most Advisable for him to apply to the Brick & Tile Makers whom (if his Machine can be made so Useful as he supposes) there is no doubt he may find Encouragement and as the Society could do nothing in this Affair, they declined Viewing the Model of the Machine'.[16]

Even some successful applicants for the Society's awards must have been out of pocket in pursuit of 'encouragement' but the high regard in which the Society came to be held ensured that its approbation carried with it a degree of public esteem that could be the greater reward.

2

'Profit and honour are two sharp spurs which quicken invention'

In November 1774 a Peter Debaufre complained to 'The Hon[bl] Gentlemen of the Arts and Sciences' that he held a patent and that one of his journeymen had devised a tool which infringed the patent and had applied to the Society for an award in respect of it. His patent had been obtained 'after great trouble and Expences and a Dispute for Eight month, with the cost of 130£ Expence to Defend the patent, beside 80£ more to the government the prize of the Patent for 14 year'.[1] Peter Debaufre appears to have provided the young Society of Arts with a novel problem, but the incident has more general interest by reason of his statement that the patent cost him £210 (in 1768/9 values) and took eight months to obtain. This statement provides a glimpse of the costs involved in obtaining a patent in 1768/9.

Although the fees to be paid by a patent petitioner (and the more variable stamp duties) may be extracted from official records, it is only from such information as Peter Debaufre lodged with the Society that the true cost may be determined. Probably the most detailed account available of early eighteenth century patenting costs comes from a notebook kept by a Lancashire linen manufacturer, Samuel Taylor. At a little over £125 he appears to have disbursed less than Peter Debaufre, but in pursuit of his grant he was away from his business on the outskirts of Manchester for nearly six months at what indirect cost cannot be known.[2]

Samuel Taylor's sojourn in London was taken up by waiting upon lawyers, clerks and officials: 'Tuesday the 30 Octob [1772] – This day we gott a warrant from the Solicitor [-

General] to sommons us and our adversary's to meet on Monday next att six att night.' 'Monday Nov the 5 – This day we waited for a hearing before the Solicitor but he could not be att leasure'. Whether an official (high or low) would be available to attend to his part in the many stages in the patent-granting process depended very much on how greatly members of an official's chambers received 'encouragement' to press upon their superiors the urgency of the petitioner's case. On his way to London Samuel Taylor had taken care to stop off in Leek where he 'gave Mr. Mils Ld. Chancellors steward' a guinea.[3] (The Lord Chancellor, the Earl of Macclesfield, had a base in Leek where he was born and was Lord of the Manor). When assent for a patent grant had finally been given, the terms of the grant were inscribed on parchment to which the Great Seal of the realm had to be appended in the presence of the Lord Chancellor – when he was 'att leasure'.*

The patent-granting process of the eighteenth century took little heed of the nature or novelty of an invention unless opposition was entered (as happened to both Peter Debaufre and Samuel Taylor). It then fell to one of the Law Officers to determine whether the petition should proceed. All that is known of Samuel Taylor's invention is that it had to do with linen yarn production. No written description was required or provided, but because of opposition from other Lancashire spinners a model had to be prepared, explained to the Solicitor-General and the claim that the invention differed from what had been known before defended. However, in the 1730s Law Officers established a practice of calling for a written description to be provided in respect of all petitions. Initially for Law Officers' convenience only, these written descriptions ('specifications') took on greater significance over time.[4] Copies of specifications were enrolled on the patent rolls and public copies could be prepared from them by clerks of the enrolment offices on request. As no indexes were kept and any of at least three enrolment offices could be the repository, discovering what patents had been granted relative to any particular subject was no light task. When the Society of Arts' Assistant Secretary was

* A list of patent procurement expenses in 1814/15 is set out in Appendix 1.

ordered in 1756 'to procure a Copy of the Patent to Paul Nightingale, with the Description or Specification thereto'[5] it was but the first of many such expeditions. On this occasion the bill to be paid to the appropriate office was £2/-/4d.*

Having obtained a grant the patentee's problems were not over. In order to exploit the monopoly gained at great cost and trouble several alternatives were available, such as persuading others to use the device or process on condition that they paid for the privilege, selling all rights in the grant to an entrepreneur with capital, entering into association with financial backers who would receive a share of the proceeds, or working it personally which would involve further personal investment. Thomas Savery had influential backers to help with his steam pump patent. These formed a company which, with legal assistance, was quick to threaten or prosecute infringers. On the other hand, John Kay's improvement in weaving looms, being comparatively simple to make, was widely pirated and the financial cost of pursuing infringers eventually became prohibitive. Richard Arkwright successfully challenged some who ignored his patent but lost when would-be free users of his devices combined against him. Boulton and Watt only began court proceedings when they felt driven to it by reason of widespread infringement making a mockery of their patent.[6]

Having regard to the costs and uncertainties associated with petitioning for a patent and to the general aversion to monopolies of this kind, it is not surprising to find how sparse were the grants sought and obtained. Prior to the Society of Arts' foundation they were usually in single figures annually. Because numbers were so low variation between years is all the more noticeable, for example, in 1754 there were nine grants, in 1756 only three. (This 1756 figure was as low as any in the previous forty years, 1719 (2) and 1736 (0) excepted.) Why when the annual average for the years 1691–95 had been eight did the corresponding figure for the 1701–10 decade fall to two? It is difficult to conceive of anything useful being deduced

* A list of official fees, stamp duties etc. paid at various offices in 1826 is given in Appendix IIA. Changes made between 1754 and 1850 were relatively minor. Appendix IIB sets out some other expenses of an official nature.

from such small and erratic numbers. One thing may however be said of them with certainty – they bear no relation whatever to the amount of innovative activity taking place in the first half of the eighteenth century.

Henry Baker's father-in-law, Daniel Defoe, recorded a quite different scene from that which it would be all too easy to imagine if based on patent statistics. His *Tour through the whole Island of Great Britain* shows the country as it appeared to a skilled observer who was also a man of business. It is a country of trade and manufacture and of economic development. 'New discoveries in metals, mines and minerals' he writes, 'new undertakings in trade, engines, manufactures, in a nation pushing and improving as we are; these things open new scenes every day, and make England especially shew a new and differing face in many places, on every occasion of surveying it.' (A quarter of a century before Defoe's *Tour*, John Carey had written enthusiastically of *The State of England* in which 'new projections are every day set on foot.)[7] It is clear from Defoe and Carey and also from many who have more recently made detailed studies of the history of technical and industrial developments, that the Society of Arts was not born into a stagnant land. Although patchy in respect both of locations and industries and with much – indeed the greater part – unrecorded, there was innovation in plenty.

Northampton, from which William Shipley published his 'Proposals' in 1753 (which led to the formation of the Society of Arts), was an excellent example of England on the move. It was a bustling market town in an area where novel agricultural appliances were available, where an old centre of town corn-mill had been converted to the production of cotton yarn by machinery, where – in one of the country's earliest infirmaries – medical practices were effected under more humane conditions than was at the time common, where the health-giving advantages of providing fresh clean air in buildings housing large numbers of people were advocated, and in which a philosophical society met to discuss the latest scientific and technical advances including demonstrations with the latest electrical and other experimental apparatus.[8] It was against this background of progressive activity that Shipley set out his 'Proposals' 'to enlarge Science, to refine Art, to improve our Manufactures,

PROPOSALS for raiſing by Subſcription a Fund to be diſtributed in Præmiums for the promoting of LIBERAL ARTS and SCIENCES, MANUFACTURES, &c.

AS Riches are acknowledged to be the Strength, Arts and Sciences may juſtly be eſteemed the Beauty of Nations. Few Kingdoms have ever been illuſtrious without the one, or formidable without the other; nor very conſiderable without both. — Does it not then behove every Nation to cultivate and promote amongſt the Members of her own Community what is ſo apparently and eminently conducive to her Intereſt and Glory? Encouragement is much the ſame to Arts and Sciences as Manuring is to the Ground, or Watering to Vegetables: They always advance and flouriſh in Proportion to the Honours they acquire or the Rewards they obtain.—Were not the *Auguſtan* and ſome ſucceeding Ages remarkable for the Delicacy of their Taſte, and the Nobleneſs of their Productions? Have they not recommended and endeared themſelves to all Poſterity by many valuable Monuments of Genius and Induſtry? None I preſume will imagine that the Men of thoſe Times were endued with natural Abilities ſuperior to the reſt of Mankind. But their Abilities, originally equal, roſe to this Superiority, by falling into a more fertile Soil, and exciting themſelves under a more favourable Influence. Had the ſame Advantages been enjoyed, even in the moſt ſupine and barbarous Periods, there is no doubt but Genius would have ſhone, and Induſtry toil'd, and very probably with equal Succeſs.

As Profit and Honour are two ſharp Spurs, which quicken Invention, and animate Application, it is humbly propoſed, That a Scheme be ſet on foot for giving both theſe Encouragements to the liberal Sciences, to the polite Arts, and to every uſeful Manufactury. That with this View a Fund be raiſed by Subſcription for the Diſtribution of ſome acceptable Præmium or honorary Gratification to any and every Work of diſtinguiſhed Ingenuity. That whoever ſhall make the moſt conſiderable Progreſs in any Branch of beneficial Knowledge, or exhibit the moſt compleat Performance in any Species of mechanick Skill; whoever ſhall contrive the beſt Expedient or execute the happieſt Project for the Comfort, the Embelliſhment, the Intereſt, or in Time of Danger, for the Defence of *Great Britain*, may receive a Reward ſuitable to the Merit of his Services. Such a Scheme, it is thought, may eaſily be eſtabliſh.d and as eaſily ſupported by a few generous and publick-ſpirited Perſons, and it is hoped may prove an effectual Means to embolden Enterprize, to enlarge Science, to refine Art, to improve our Manufactures, and extend our Commerce; in a Word, to render *Great Britain* the School of Inſtruction, as it is already the Centre of Traffick to the whole World.

Northampton June, 8. 1753.

Proposals that gave rise to the Society of Arts as advertised by William Shipley in the *Northampton Mercury*, 8 June 1753.

and extend our Commerce'. Though phrased in patriotic terms his objective went beyond a narrow nationalism; it was 'to render Great Britain a school of instruction as it is already the centre of traffic to the greatest part of the known world'.[9]

Shipley's proposition was that 'Profit and honour are two sharp spurs which quicken invention and animate application' and 'Arts and Sciences ... always advance and flourish in proportion to the rewards they acquire, and the honours they obtain'. When, more than a century later, Abraham Lincoln said of the patent system that it 'added the fuel of interest to the fire of genius', he was stating more narrowly what Shipley expressed broadly.

Shipley's England was still predominantly agricultural and in his time agriculture had little use for patents. There is a view that his scheme was most successful in agriculture; that the Society had successes in agriculture is clear but there may have been greater successes in other spheres than is superficially manifest.

One of the Society's great and lasting agricultural concerns was the encouragement of the 'new husbandry' of Jethro Tull. On this Robert Dossie, early recorder of the Society's achievements, gave as his opinion: 'Mr. Tull ... only started the notion. The practice was very little pursued till the Society awakened the public attention to it by their premiums'.[10] It may be that regarded in the long term the Society also awakened public attention in the mechanical and other technical arts in ways not immediately apparent. There is an interesting coincidence of timing in relation to patent figures that may not be without significance. Patent grants by decades for the eighteenth century were:[11]

1700–09 ...	21	1750–59 ...	79
1710–19 ...	37	1760–69 ...	191
1720–29 ...	89	1770–79 ...	296
1730–39 ...	55	1780–89 ...	474
1740–49 ...	74	1790–99 ...	643
		(1800–09 ...	1,569)

For the five years 1760–64 the figure was 65; for 1765–69 it was 126. On the basis of these figures it is evident that patent numbers took off approximately ten years after the Society's foundation. This may be pure coincidence or there may be political, social or economic reasons that have not yet been pinpointed. There is no question, however, that the Society was a success story during its first ten years in terms of membership and income. Equally rapidly it built up a high and countrywide reputation. It was an association of influential and respected people that had gained widely-felt authority and beyond question it 'awakened the public attention' to a wide variety of matters. There may well have been many who did not consciously relate their innovative ideas to the Society's offers but who nevertheless moved in a climate of improvement-seeking generated at least in part by the Society.

As indicated earlier, several recipients of premiums took out patents after receiving awards from the Society. There may have been an element of greed in so doing but another aspect of this behaviour lies in the value of the approbation of the Society, for it could be regarded as such proof of merit in an invention as to encourage the devisor to risk the costs and hazards of petitioning for a patent grant.* Other than for very small improvements, the expense of time and treasure required to devise, test and develop an invention must in many cases have made the Society's awards appear a poor recompense to some who had initially been stimulated by the attraction of its offers.

The upsurge in patenting did not go unnoticed by contemporaries. In 1776 an unnamed rhymester published a poem of seventy-odd lines the tenor of which may be gathered from a few illustrative samples:[12] (See also Appendix III)

Hail to the Patent! Which enables man
To vend a folio – or a warming pan.
This makes the windlass work with double force,
And smoke jacks whirl more rapid in their course;
Confers a sanction on the doctor's pill,
Oft' known to cure, but oft'ner known to kill.

Hail to the Patent! That at Irwin's shop
Improves the flavour of a currant-drop.
This too can make an engine squirt so high,
As to o'er flow the parlour next the sky,
That he who sleeps, shall wake and start amain,
And think the gen'ral deluge come again.

* The Society could not readily prevent misuse of its awards scheme by patentees. However circumstances arose from time to time in which practices were drawn to the attention of the public by advertisements in journals or newspapers. (See Appendices IV and V.)

One of the points of interest from the poem is that several of the subjects mentioned do not relate to patents then in force though still remembered as patented objects, for example, the engine squirting high would be Thomas Savery's, the patent in respect of which had expired almost half a century earlier. The doctor's pill, later in the poem referred to as 'Justly-Famous Pills', was no doubt, Dr. Richard James's fever cure for which the patent had expired. (Dr. James had a later patent for pills but as they had been available for less than two years at the date of the poem they did not merit the epithet 'Justly-Famous'.) Other patented materials appear to have a somewhat trivial aspect, such as: 'The Patent that at Irwin's shop improves the flavour of a currant-drop'; 'Genuine Patent Blacking Cakes [that] Gloss'd the poet's shoes so that they shone as brightly as in the *Morning Post*', while wigs were 'patent-made, and lake of patent hair'.

So another point to be taken from the poem is that many patents were sought and obtained for apparent trivia – flavoured throat pastilles, shoe polish, perfumed toilet water, smoke jacks and cheap metal 'toys' – in spite of the costs involved in obtaining them. It is clear that then, as now, the costs of patenting could be money well spent for commodities sold in large numbers. Further, there is no doubt that to proclaim 'Manufactured under His Majesty's Royal Letters Patent' was a useful selling ploy when vending to a public unaware that nothing more was required of a petitioner for a patent than a willingness to pay the statutory fees and stamp duties – and the unscheduled gratuities. When Peter Debaufre was invited to state his case before the Society he took along a printed copy of his patent embellished with the royal arms, a document which would probably make a far greater impression on would-be customers than it did on the gentlemen of the Society. (No official prints were issued by the patent authorities at the time so that which Peter Debaufre handed in to the Society would be prepared at his own whim and expense.)

An aspect of the patent system briefly mentioned above was also referred to in the poem – 'Patents are obtained as fancy wills' though 'he who keeps the seal, will not remit the fee'. For most petitioners patents were obtained for the asking provided the appropriate fees and duties were paid – the final senior functionary in a long line being the Lord Chancellor in whose presence the patent document was sealed. There was no enquiry into the novelty of the alleged invention, no check on its practicability or efficacy, nor any other form of examination. Only following objection by a third party was a form of enquiry gone through, usually before one of the Law Officers. The parties involved were called in to state their positions, as in the cases of Samuel Taylor and Peter Debaufre; the usual outcome being that the application proceeded 'at the petitioner's risk', that is, it was left to the Privy Council or the Courts to settle the matter after grant if opponents chose to pursue their objections to such lengths.

In contrast with the patent system's failure to examine applications were the careful enquiries carried out by the Society before bestowing awards. These are recorded in the Minutes and elsewhere[13] and a remarkable tribute was paid to them in 1851 in the course of proceedings before a House of Lords' Select Committee. Asked a question regarding the possibility of a fraud being carried out on a patent petitioner during the long delay between application and grant by a third party depositing a model of the petitioner's invention in the Society's repository (thus disclosing it to the public prior to grant), a witness replied that the Society of Arts would investigate whether, indeed, the third party was the true and first inventor. The Committee then went on to consider whether 'a Board such as the Society of Arts' might be established to investigate alleged inventions.[14]

Reverting to the 1776 poem, several of the patented materials alluded to appear to have been creations of Society members. There was the pill 'oft' known to cure ...' a nostrum of the celebrated Dr. Richard James; the flavoured currant drop doubtless emanated from the Society's Dr. Irwin; a 'Pinchbeck' mentioned would relate to Christopher Pinchbeck, a Chairman of the Committee of Mechanics with three patents to his name. Indeed, by 1776 there were many patentee members; for example, three patents for optical devices were the basis on which a long-enduring business was built by two early members, John and Peter Dollond; John Wilkinson, 'Chief Manager of the Iron Works at Wrexham' was already a patentee when Samuel More proposed him for membership (eight further patents were added to his tally later). Immediately following his election Wilkinson suggested that encouragement be given towards 'the making of bar iron with pit coal' for which Dr. John Roebuck, then of Birmingham but later of Carron Iron Works fame, received an award although a member of the Society and forthwith took out a patent for the same subject; Joseph Bramah did not take out his first patent until 1778 but followed it with eighteen more, several of which were acquired while he was a Chairman of the Committee of Mechanics. These were but a few of many Society members possessing patents (see, for example, Appendix VI.)

Notwithstanding the personal interest in patents exhibited by an increasing number of members – especially among those of a mechanical turn of mind – as the eighteenth century progressed towards and into the nineteenth, the Society was careful to maintain blue water between its award schemes and the patent system. 'It is one of our Laws never to meddle with any Thing for which Patents are granted',* wrote Samuel More in 1771 for the Society to a correspondent with thoughts of taking out a patent for a device for which he also sought the Society's interest.[15] ('Never to meddle' with patents is a noticeably milder phrase than the 'it is contrary to the Institution and Design of the Society to encourage the obtaining of Patents' of the 1758 letter cited earlier.) The extent to which the Society was prepared to go to avoid 'meddling' in patent matters could not be better illustrated than in its dealings with the Board of Trade.

An amicable and at times fruitful relationship had been established between the Society and the Committee of the Privy Council for Trade, the Society's opinion being sought on a number of matters. In February 1791 a collection of documents was received from the Board relating to a matter for

* The Society could, however, bend its 'Laws' on humanitarian issues. Recognising the importance of limiting the spread of fires in domestic and other property and convinced of the efficacy of a patented fire extinguisher, the Society went to great expense and a remarkable amount of trouble in 1761 to stage a public demonstration of the device. See Hudson and Luckhurst, *The Royal Society of Arts 1754–1954*, pp.108–109.

which a patent was sought. This evoked the response 'the Society are fully sensible of the Honour their Lordships intended ... but not having it in their power consistently with their Rules and Orders, to appoint a Select Committee, and a Member having declared in His Place that one of the Papers referred contains an Account of the Process, which if generally divulged may be injurious to the Party applying for a Patent, the Society cannot take the said papers into consideration'. Six years later when the Board proposed to refer an invention to examination by the Society, Samuel More pointed out that the Society could not 'enquire into any Discovery for which the Inventor intended to apply for a patent'.[16]

The Society's 'Rules and Orders' regarding patents began to take formal shape in 1763 when the Minutes for the 13th April recorded the annually repeated motion ordering Premium Books to be printed. That motion was followed, without antecedent reference to any discussion, by:

> 'A Motion was made, That a N.B. be inserted at the end of the Book of Premiums, That no Person will be admitted a Candidate for any Premium offered by this Society, who has obtained a Patent for the exclusive Right of making or performing any Thing for which such Premium is offered. – Agreed to.'

A proposal three years later to impose stricter conditions on Candidates was rejected; this took the following lines: 'Whoever gains any Premium should, if required by the Society, Enter into an Engagement not to obtain any Patent for its Performance.' The 1763 rule remained in force as before but in 1780 it was agreed that after 'obtained' in the 'N.B.' 'or proposes to obtain' should be inserted. Other motions came up for discussion from time to time that did not, or did not materially, affect what had been decided in 1763.

Affirmation of the 1763 'N.B.' was made in 1769 when, during revision of the rules affecting premiums, it was decided to add to the book of *Rules and Orders*

> 'No Persons shall receive any Premium Bounty or Encouragement from the Society for any Matter for which he has obtained a Patent.'

This rule qualified the Society's awards offers for more than eighty years.

The *Rules and Orders* received further amendment in November 1794 when the following was included, 'nor shall any Model or Machine for which a Patent has been obtained or is proposed to be obtained be admitted to the Repository of the Society'. An addition affecting members was agreed in March 1798: 'No member who has obtained a Patent for any Article similar to such as may be produced to the Society shall be allowed to vote either in the Committee or Society on that Subject.'*

In the preface to the Society's *Transactions* for 1802 (Vol.XX) opportunity was taken in a passage referring to conditions relating to awards to compare advantageously to the Society the merits of its system as against the hazards of patenting: 'It may be necessary to remark, that no Patent Machines are admitted to a place in their Repository; it is one of the conditions on which the gifts of the Society are conferred that the inventor accepts the reward and honourable mention of the Society, in full compensation for a patent right: the inventor has, however, full liberty to make and vend his inventions and it is natural to suppose, that the applications of the Public for such articles will be made to him, in preference to others; and that the sanction of the Society will bring his merits forward to the world, in a manner likely to procure him much future benefit.† Several decisions lately made in the Courts of Justice, show upon what futile grounds many of the Patents stand which have been granted, and that instead of producing any profit to the Patentee, they have involved him in great expense and trouble; whereas the rewards of this Society are granted free of every expense and the inventor's name is recorded and handed down to posterity.'[17]

* This Rule formally acknowledged the existence of patentee-members of the Society. They were, in fact, quite numerous by this time relative to the total membership of the Society. (Examples are given in Appendix VI.)

† The relevant passages from *Rules and Orders* for 1802 – operative for a least half a century following – are given in Appendix VII with a related passage from a 'Notice to Candidates' of 1841 extracted from *Transactions* Vol.LIII.

This roseate view of the Society's awards scheme is heightened by reference to risks inherent in the obvious alternative. These risks were real and severe. To go to the expense and trouble of pursuing a petition for the royal grant only to be met with a lack of interest when eventually the patented invention was offered to the public was frustrating, but to be successful in laying before the public 'a long-felt want' could be ruinously costly as well as frustrating. The greater the success, the greater the likelihood of infringement. Determined infringers would not desist from their activities without threat of legal proceedings and even success in proceedings before the Courts could be at a price that could not be recouped. In addition, there was always a risk that due to uncertainties in the law relating to patents an appearance before the Courts could result in loss of the patent. There was minimal statute law and little case law to guide the judges in 1802. But one thing they knew, and knew full well – as a general principle monopolies were against the public interest.

3

'A series of formulas so antiquated that the origin of them is lost in the obscurity of past centuries ...'

The English system of patents of invention was a hybrid thing grafted in the reign of Elizabeth I. A few sports may be remarked earlier but regular cultivation only began after 1550. A practice formalised in Venice nearly a century before to encourage ingenious artisans by offers of limited monopolies was implanted on a centuries-old English system of grants of royal favours. It was a simple arrangement whereby the introduction of new manufactures could be stimulated without cost to the exchequer. Letters patent (letters of the sovereign open to be read by anyone) had long been employed as vehicles for granting titles, lands, dispensations and other privileges.[1]

Such an exercise of the royal prerogative could not be subject to consideration or control by the courts and, apart from minor procedural Acts, was not defined by statute or case law until the so-called 'Statute of Monopolies' of 1624 (introduced following abuses of the system) banned all monopolies except certain existing specified grants and 'any letters patent and grants of privilege for the term of fourteen years or under hereafter to be made of the sole working or making of any manner of new manufacture within this Realm to the true and first inventor and inventors of such manufactures ...'

Petitioning for letters patent had developed into a complex ritual long before the reign of Elizabeth I. Fabricated over centuries by step by step additions of checks and counterchecks for the avoidance of misuse of the Great Seal, by the mid-sixteenth century the stages through which a petition had to pass were extensive. The same procedures applied in the mid-eighteenth and mid-nineteenth centuries.

The 1624 Statute had laid down that matters affecting monopoly grants were to be determined by the common laws but, notwithstanding, over the next hundred years few patent matters went before the courts. For reasons not entirely clear an action in 1724 relating to Dr. Richard James' fever cure patent appears to have been the last to be handled by the Privy Council (petitions to extend the lives of patents excepted). From then on the Courts dealt with patent issues, though initially with few precedent cases to guide them.

Coincidence it may have been but matters affecting Society of Arts' members stand out as leading cases over the remainder of the century. When John Dollond's patent of 1758 for 'Making object-glasses of refracting telescopes' came before the Courts it resulted in some important points being settled.[2] What was perhaps the most important patent law case of the century was that of *Liardet v. Johnson* in 1788; this also involved Society members. In 1773 John Liardet was granted a patent for 'Cement for building purposes' (No. 1040) and the builders of the Society's house in the Adelphi took a substantial interest in it, so much so that the patented material was marketed as 'Adams' Oil Cement'. As joint plaintiffs with Liardet in an unsuccessful action 'Messrs. Adams of the Adelphi' incurred a serious financial set-back.[3] The Court held the specification to be obscure and incomplete and, in so doing, laid down that the main tests of validity of a patent were to be applied to the specification. This was new and marked a turning point in patent procedure. The essential phrase in the judgement was

> 'the condition of giving encouragement is this: that you must specify upon record your invention in such a way as shall teach an artist, when your term is out, to make it – and to make it as well as you by your directions.'[4]

As mentioned earlier, in the first quarter of the eighteenth century written descriptions were occasionally called for by Law Officers as a condition of allowing petitions to proceed. From the mid 1730s these descriptions ('specifications') became a regular feature of the system even though there was no statutory basis for them. They comprised nothing more than a Law

John Street (later renamed as John Adam Street) part of the Adam Brothers' extensive Adelphi development as engraved by Thomas Malton in 1792. The Society of Arts' House is on the left; adjoining premises beyond were acquired by the Society during the last century.

Officers' requirement with the object of distinguishing in a very general manner the new from the old. How much information ought to be provided was not made clear. Between insistence on a specification being provided and Lord Mansfield's pronouncement in *Liardet v. Johnson* more than forty years passed. It was a pronouncement that opened the way to the modern patent system but few of the specifications prepared before it would have passed the Mansfield test and, since it was to apply to the specification of any patent already granted, it had the effect of retrospective legislation – as Richard Arkwright and James Watt, among others, discovered.

On hearing in 1781 that Arkwright had lost a verdict due to inadequacies of specification, Watt wrote in alarm to his partner Boulton, 'Though I do not love Arkwright I don't like the precedent of setting aside patents through default of specification. I fear for our own ... I begin to have little faith in patents ...' He and Boulton had reason to be fearful. They delayed taking action against infringers as long as they felt they could. Eventually, when they considered they could delay no longer without having their patent regarded as a meaningless parchment, they ventured into six years of litigation concluded by a favourable verdict arrived at by special pleading and an exceptional disregard of the Mansfield test.[5]

Revocation of Arkwright's grant sent shock waves through the patenting community. Josiah Wedgwood wrote in his Common Place Book, 'The first time of meeting Mr. Arkwright was in London and after he had lost his patent trial I attended a meeting of patent holders at his lodgings'.[6] Wedgwood was later to bring Arkwright to Watt (no small achievement in view of Watt's earlier antipathetic attitude to Arkwright) for discussion of a draft of proposals for patent reform prepared by Watt. Although a more polished form of these proposals was presented to the Lord Chancellor in 1790 it was an unavailing exercise. However, Watt's scheme for reform stands on record as the first carefully thought-through and lucidly expressed plan for patent reform.[7]

The nineteenth century opened with several attempts to bring patents to the notice of Parliament but, in the midst of a major war, the Government's attention was taken up with other matters. The war over, industrial disturbance and social unrest (Peterloo and all that) preoccupied political minds, although many attempts were made through 1819 to 1829 (and beyond) to bring in reforming Bills. 1829 stands out as a year in which some appearance of attention to inventors' problems was given when a Select Committee of the House of Commons was appointed to inquire into the state of the patent laws. This Committee received a large amount of oral and written evidence which is now of far greater value to historians than any benefit that accrued to inventors at the time. A procession of chemists and engineers of standing, lawyers, patent agents and civil servants (many, if not most, of whom were Society of Arts members) gave their diverse opinions of what was wrong, but with few useful suggestions for righting wrongs. In the event, it is hardly surprising that the Committee's report was brief, consisting of little more than the following: 'The subject referred to the consideration of Your Committee [is] in its nature so intricate and important, that ... they are only prepared to report the Minutes of the Evidence.' The Committee did, however, 'earnestly recommend to The House that the inquiry may be resumed early in the next Session'.[8] It was not resumed at the next session, nor for many sessions following.

This 1829 Parliamentary Inquiry made manifest to all what had been glaringly obvious to some. The problems besetting the patent system were 'intricate and important' but there was also a dearth of ideas regarding improvements, and such as there were were so disparate as to be irreconcilable. In addition, there were influential groups for whom the existing arrangements provided comfortable sources of income to be defended strenuously.

Reporting back to his masters in 1814 on aspects of English industry and manufactures, a Prussian civil servant observed, 'A patent costs £100. The authority which grants the patent gets only £20. The rest of the money is paid in fees and perquisites to various officials and other persons. But anyone who knows the ropes can save between £20 and £30 ...'[9]

'Factory Commissioner' Johann May may not have been accurately informed on financial details but he had grasped the most essential fact concerning a patent application – it was important to be in touch with 'someone who knew the ropes'. Although a saving on application costs was always desirable, there were times – as when a competitor was hard on one's heels – when reducing procedure times was of the essence. Then acquaintance of people 'who knew the ropes' could be vital. Foremost among such people were clerks in the various procedural offices. One was James Poole who, at the time of Johann May's inquiries, had held a position in the Attorney-General's Patent Office for 38 years. When he died in 1817 his son, Moses, 'inherited' the position. Although he does not appear to have entered into membership, James maintained contacts with the Society of Arts throughout his years of patent duties. Moses, however, joined the Society very soon after entering into his 'inheritance' and paid subscriptions for more than twenty years.

Moses Poole became the most active agent for the obtaining of patents. By 1820 he and the Clerk of the Petty Bag, Francis Abbott had cornered most of the business. (The involvement of the Office of the Petty Bag in the patent process lay in there being three distinct places of enrolment for specifications. Other enrolment offices were the Six Clerks' Office and the Chapel of the Rolls, but after the latter was opened to the public in 1849 most specifications were presented at the other two repositories so that officials there could still receive fees.) Poole and Abbott conducted patent applications through their many stages from petition to sealed grant. They did not draft specifications; this was the business of people with technical expertise, such as the Society's Arthur Aikin if the invention were of a chemical nature, or Society members John Farey, Thomas Gill or W.H. Wyatt if mechanical.

About 1840 Moses Poole entered into more regular association with a civil/mechanical engineer specification-drafter who had also read for the Bar. This was William Carpmael whose election in 1842 began a family connection with the Society of Arts that continued for well over a century. The Poole/Carpmael partnership was on a winning ticket, taking a leading role in the patent agency business from its beginning and laying sure foundations for a practice that still provides services to the patenting public.[10]

Poole and Carpmael, Francis Abbott and others finding profitable employment in the system as it then was had little interest in patent reform. William Carpmael, a redoubtable expert witness in the Courts, was no less forthright as a witness in other situations; before a Parliamentary Inquiry he gave his opinion firmly – patent reform was a non-starter.[11] A Manchester patent agent writing in 1854, after a measure of reform had been achieved, told of his personal uphill strivings:

> 'Although these evils [of the patent system] were so palpable, so numerous, and so unsuited to the wants and circumstances of the times, the difficulty of obtaining their repeal or amendment was much greater than future generations will believe. I had been convinced of the necessity of an alteration for many years, but found it impossible to meet with any one willing to join me in the trouble and expense of agitating the subject until the Great Exhibition project was fairly launched. This I considered a favourable opportunity for making an impression, both on the public mind and on the legislature. I appealed to many of my brethren in the profession, but generally received for answer, "That it was not our business, that it ought to proceed from the public, that the old law answered our interests very well, therefore I ought to let well alone". I was met this way by the Patent Agents both in London and the country and, indeed, nearly all the periodicals devoted to patented inventions advocated the old absurd system, or a slight modification of it.'[12]

The writer of this passage did not pursue his efforts towards reform in quite so bleak a climate as he would have his readers believe. The 'leave well alone' attitude he found among his fellow patent agents was not as prevalent in other sections of the community. Attitudes were changing and, in the event, not least in Manchester. In 1782 the Manchester Committee for the Protection of Trade had declared itself ready to take strong action 'so as to prevent the pernicious effects of patents'.[13] Superficially at least it would appear that in Manchester in or about 1825 there was a conversion so dramatic as to bear comparison with that on the Damascus road long ago when a blinding light illumined a mind previously closed, for the Chamber of Commerce announced that 'Patents had become desirable, most especially at a period when the manufacturers of this country have to sustain an active competition with the production of foreign industries'. The patent system, said the Manchester Chamber, 'should be made as perfect as its nature will admit'.[14] This pronouncement was followed up in 1828 by the formation of a Patent Reform Committee, though this made little, if any, progress. However, another committee set up in 1851 contributed significantly to the national groundswell building up towards patent reform. (This 1851 Committee consisted principally of engineers, that is, machine makers, as distinct from the 1782 Committee for the Protection of Trade comprised in the main of cotton spinners anxious to use patented machines without paying royalties; Manchester's 'conversion' probably had more to do with changes in technology than changes of opinion!)

More activity was, in fact, directed towards patent reform in the first half of the nineteenth century than is evident to any but the most diligent researcher. Throughout a couple of decades from 1819, Bills, Petitions and Inquiries relating to patents occupied Parliamentary time, though with little result.[15] One Bill did, however, make its way onto the Statute Book under the guidance of Lord Brougham. Seen against the magnitude of the problems and the many-sided issues to be addressed, this piece of legislation seemed (and still seems) a mere trifling nod towards change.[16] Notwithstanding, this 1835 enactment has historic significance for it was the first relating to patents since the Statute of 1624. Things were on the move!

That it was Lord Brougham who persisted in pressing forward with this reforming Bill in a difficult climate is of especial significance having regard to happenings at the Society of Arts. In his history of the Society, Henry Trueman Wood quotes a story of how Lord Brougham 'on one occasion attending a meeting of the Society, went off with an outspoken declaration as to what he hoped might be his final fate if he ever wasted his time with a Society that spent all its time in discussing "rules and orders".' 'Thus was lost to the Society', observed Wood, 'the energy afterwards expended in promoting the Society for the Diffusion of Useful Knowledge and the Social Science Association' (and – Wood could have added – patent reform).[17]

This was no new criticism. Others had long before been concerned by the extent of the apparently fruitless discussions into which the Society's general meetings could – and often did

– degenerate. Free and open discussion of its affairs to which all members could contribute served the Society well in its earliest years but it was a form of conducting business that gave free reign to the pedantic, the loquacious, or the tendentious to take up time that could have been better employed in considering if and/or how the Society should change with changing times.

When that most diligent, versatile and intellectually well-equipped of the Society's Secretaries, Samuel More, died in 1799 after adding lustre to his office and to the Society for fully thirty years, the Society's standing was high in the land – and in some other lands. While More's death may be regarded as marking a watershed in the Society's fortunes, the decline that was so alarmingly apparent forty years later had little to do with the Secretaryship. In terms of income to be distributed in awards the Society had peaked before More became its Secretary. By the time of his death annual income was less than a half of what it had been when he was appointed to that office.[18] Among many factors responsible for this fall in income was that the industrial scene had changed and the concept of offering small money prizes to encourage innovation seemed less of a good idea than fifty years earlier.

No less significant to the Society's future situation was the founding of the Royal Institution in the year of More's death. 'At the 1799 meeting for the distribution of awards, the members of the Society of Arts were informed by their Secretary "of another Institution, lately begun ... for promoting Mechanical and Chemical knowledge ... [which] ought not to be considered as tending to injure this Institution"'.[19] Not More's last words, but words that indicated that, whatever his great merits, he was no prophet. Although the original intention may have been the training of mechanics in basic science, the appointment of Humphrey Davy as its first scientific lecturer soon made the Institution a fashionable centre, drawing in members of society that in earlier times may well have been happy to be known as associated with the older institution at the Adelphi. This was but the first of several organisations with allied objectives that sprang into being over the next forty years.

Brougham's Society for the Diffusion of Useful Knowledge

and the Social Science Association operated alongside the London Mechanics' Institution which numbered among its foundation members Bryan Donkin, a Vice-President of the Society of Arts and John Millington, Professor of Mechanics at the Royal Institution and for nearly a quarter of a century a Society of Arts member. In 1832 the National Gallery of Practical Science with its display of industrial objects supplemented by brief lectures was opened, to be quickly followed by the Royal Gallery of Arts and Sciences (later known as the Polytechnic Institution) backed by several members of Parliament. 'The potential for the advancement of practical knowledge that such institutions represented was seemingly as enormous as their supposed constituency, and there appeared to be room for any number of them ... like the Adelaide Gallery when it first opened, the Polytechnic, which received a royal charter in 1839 was a kind of modernised Society of Arts, dedicated to encouraging inventors by giving free space and publicity, though no prizes, to the machines and models they sent in.'[20]

Arthur Aikin, appointed to the Secretaryship in 1817, was aware that the Society must change with changing times and proposed a course of lectures on manufactures and the reading of papers for discussion at meetings. 'From 1829, when the scheme was first started, to 1842, after he had resigned the Secretaryship, he continued to deliver year after year, excellent and well-illustrated courses on various branches of manufactures.' Aikin probably sought to bring about more fundamental changes but 'he could never get his ideas properly supported by influential members of the Society'. He has, however, been credited with the initiation – though not fully effected in his lifetime – of 'a change in the Society's methods, which ultimately had the result of turning the Society from a purely premium-giving body into one whose main object became the dissemination of information about the industrial arts and sciences, and the publication of new discoveries and inventions of an industrial character'.[21]

Active and able though Aikin was, he could not stem the decline that had set in long before he took office. His resignation in 1839 was followed by events relating to the appointment of a new Secretary that nearly did mortal damage to the Society.

That the appointment of a new Secretary should create what would now be called 'media-interest' is an indication that the Society, however low its fortunes had fallen, still retained no small measure of public esteem. Some technical publications, such as *The Mechanics' Magazine*, devoted several column inches to the subject of the Secretaryship. In reporting the meeting at which candidates (eleven in number) offered themselves and their testimonials to the consideration of the Society, the *M.M.* observed, 'It was evident to all present that the contest will be between ... Mr. Baddely ["Machinist", backed by the London Mechanics' Institute] and Mr. Williams [Secretary of the Mathematical Society]. Mr. Graham has little, if any chance of success; but he will probably be third on the poll.' ('The meeting was numerously attended, and the proceedings occupied until nearly midnight.') The *M.M.* did not attempt to conceal its dismay at the outcome of the election meeting held on 18th December (1839):

> 'The *Government* [*M.M.*italics] candidate was successful – the choice of the Society falling upon Mr. W.A. Graham, by a majority of two votes over Mr. Williams. The number of members who voted for Mr. Graham was 96, and for Mr. Williams 94: – the other candidates, in a sporting phrase, were "no-where" – some had not a single vote. ...
>
> By dint of private friendship and personal influence in the upper circles, where Mr. Graham has been employed as a tutor (and to his ability in which capacity nearly all his testimonials applied) and under the auspices of the first Lord of the Admiralty, he has obtained the Secretaryship; while the candidate who was supported by the whole body of those who take an active interest in the affairs of the institution, and to whom the other candidates with scientific pretensions gave place, was, as we have stated, left in a minority of **two**. It is not to be expected that Mr. Graham can work well with these members.
>
> The prosperity of the Society hinged upon the result of this election; all hopes, therefore, of its renovation and extension are now we fear at an end. ...
>
> Mr. Hume [Chairman], in addressing the Secretary elect, told him that properly to fulfil the duties that had devolved upon him, he had a most arduous task to perform ... For the good of the Society we say – may he disappoint our fears!'[22]

Mr. Graham certainly entered into a troubled inheritance. He took office with the Society's finances in poor shape. Eighteen months later those responsible for overseeing accounts reported that not merely was revenue insufficient to meet expenditure but only £400 was available to meet commitments. Proposals put forward shortly afterwards with a view to effecting economies impinged upon the Secretary's position and brought about Mr. Graham's resignation. Thereafter, 'things appear to have got into a general muddle'.[23] The Society was, indeed, in a desperate situation; it was saved, in the main, by a combination of mechanicians and engineers, legal gentlemen, and people with feet in both camps – patent practitioners. But, to use another sporting phrase from the early nineteenth century, 'it was a damn close-run thing'.

4

'The whole gang of Hanapers and Chaff-Waxes must be done away with'

The Prussian industrial intelligence officer whose information on the patent system has been mentioned made a thorough country-wide tour and his report is a remarkable record of machines and manufactures to be seen in 1814. 'In this land [England] of efficiency there is a superfluity of interesting things to be seen. There is something new to catch the eye in every step that one takes.' His eye did not miss the Society's house at the Adelphi 'where the rooms are furnished and decorated in a manner worthy of the functions held in them. Dr. Taylor, the Secretary of the Society of Arts, is most helpful to foreign visitors. Meetings are held in the Society's rooms on Mondays, Tuesdays, Thursdays and Fridays. On these days, too, the Society's collection of models and manufactured goods is open for inspection in the rooms on the ground floor'.[1] But the Society met on Wednesdays! Was Factory Commissioner May misinformed? Having stepped inside the Society's house, interviewed its Secretary, and received a conducted tour of its Repository with explanations of its contents from the member of staff 'in charge of the collection', it could hardly be that Herr May was misinformed. It would rather seem that someone had steered this technically-interested visitor away from the Wednesday evening general meetings of the Society (where the perennial discussions of Rules and Orders so disgusted Lord Brougham) to committee meetings at which lively discussions on technical matters could be expected.

The very nature of the Society's primary activities necessitated technical discussion, usually in committee by people with some expertise in the subjects at issue. As earlier indicated, almost from its foundation the Society had at its disposal panels of experts (not necessarily in membership but ready to enter into discussion and offer opinions) who met in committee or communicated with committee members by correspondence or directly. To adjudicate on the suitability for a reward of an object or process was no light matter. It was common for committees to meet many times – perhaps over periods of several months to assess the merits of a single subject.[2] This aspect of the Society's affairs has been ably set out by a former Secretary:

> 'It is necessary ... to remember that the successful operation of the Society's policy of encouraging innovation through the award of premiums depended upon a sensitive network of people (not necessarily members of the Society) and businesses, with expert knowledge and practical experience, able and willing usually without payment to advise and/or to give practical help in testing new materials and techniques. It was not a formal organization but it covered most aspects of the commercial, industrial and scientific problems of the time. While it had developed because of the Society, it was available to others. The businessmen, scientists, farmers and others assisting the Society's work benefited by the early knowledge they received of new ideas, products, materials and processes.'[3]

The Society's committees became useful meeting places for people of allied interests; for example, through the 1760s and 70s (and perhaps beyond) the names of those attending the Committee of Mechanics correspond in large measure with those of the men who gathered socially as 'The Society of Civil Engineers' from 1771 onwards.[4] By the 1820s the civil engineers were giving way to mechanical engineers and 'mechanicians'. (With the formation of the Institution of Civil Engineers in 1818 the 'Civils' were in a position to organise their own meetings for consideration of subjects specific to their interests.) Thomas Gill, for more than twenty years Chairman of the Committee of Mechanics and who could fairly be described as a mechanical engineer, commended the Society of Arts and its committees to prospective readers of *The Technical Repository* (later generally referred to as *Gill's Repository*), the periodical he launched in 1822: 'The

Communications [of the Society] are many ... particularly in that of Mechanics: insomuch, that that Committee has been under the necessity of sitting in two evenings of every week ... and, in fact, it now affords one of the best opportunities of acquiring practical information that can be met with. Its meetings, therefore, are very fully attended by Members of the Society, and also by their friends, who, under proper regulations, have the permission of being introduced'.[5] This statement throws light on what Prussian Factory Commisser May had reported in 1814 about the numerous meetings of the Society and bears upon a passage appearing in the Society's *Transactions* some years later: 'For a long time the house of the Society was the only place of meeting for certain classes of members, who found an advantage in the opportunities of discussing, with those of the same profession or calling, questions of professional interest'.[6]

Thomas Gill performed some of the functions now carried out by patent agents, as did his co-chairman for many years of the Committee of Mechanics, Bryan Donkin.[7] It may well be that people with patent interests predominated on the Society's technical committees at this period. These, it must be assumed, were included among the people to whom *The Mechanics' Magazine* referred in 1839 – 'the whole body of those who take an active interest in the affairs of the institution' and who were dismayed by the turn of events following Arthur Aikin's resignation. However, a turn of events not of their devising moved the Society onto a course favourable to them.

In the autumn of 1841 a report from the Committee of Accounts setting out the parlous state of the Society's finances resulted in the appointment of a special committee to consider the Society's straightened circumstances, their cause and possible remedy.[8] This committee, as would be expected, comprised for the most part people of good standing in the Society and more widely. Men, for example, such as George Bailey, architect and curator of the Soane Museum, who had been a Society member for twenty years and Edward Speer of the Treasury, a member from 1818, both of whom were shortly to be honoured by being elected the first Chairmen of Council. A member with an even longer record in the Society was William Tooke F.R.S. who had chaired the Committee of Correspondence as early as

1804. Tooke, a technically-minded solicitor, had helped Brougham and Birkbeck to found the Society for the Diffusion of Useful Knowledge and when MP for Taunton in the 1830s he had been active in support of Bills aimed at patent reform. John Bethell was another solicitor on the committee with technical leanings; he had built up an international business based on exploitation of some of his patented inventions. Yet another lawyer associated with the work of this committee was William Bodkin, barrister and Treasury counsel, MP for Rochester in 1841. Bodkin's later career took him to the Bench and a knighthood; he was perhaps best known in his time for his long and persistent campaign for reform of the Poor Law, though at the Society he was known for his active interest in its affairs over a great many years culminating in membership of its Council where he was an exceptionally regular attender. With people such as these available, it is more than a little surprising that the person nominated to be Chairman of the special committee was a relatively young man who had only been a member of the Society for three years; this was Thomas Webster, a Cambridge mathematician who had been performing secretarial duties for the Institution of Civil Engineers over the previous four years.[9]

Having read for the Bar while with the Civil Engineers, Webster left them on being appointed assistant to Sir William Henry Maule, QC on the latter's elevation to the Bench. Webster was called in 1841, in which year his *Law and Practice of Patents for Inventions* was published to be followed three years later by the first volume of *Reports and Notes of Cases on Letters Patent for Inventions*. Although privately prepared reports of patent actions had appeared earlier and a few were to appear later, *Webster* was the principal reference work prior to officially prepared *Reports* being introduced and continued to be the main reference source for older cases long afterwards. Webster became the foremost patent counsel of the following thirty years, taking over from Benjamin Rotch, probably the first specialist patent counsel. Rotch practised principally in the Northern Circuit (taking in the industrial areas of Lancashire and Yorkshire) and this was to become Webster's chosen field. When MP for Knaresborough in the 1830s Rotch had taken a lead in drafting a patent reform Bill. He had shown himself committed to patent reform for at least a decade before this

Bill was introduced. He was a member of the Society of Arts for well over thirty years, was active on the Committee of Mechanics and was elected a Vice-President in 1848.

The Webster committee acted speedily and tendered its report in a matter of weeks, but it was not to every Society members' liking and did not gain acceptance until the spring of 1843. Constitutionally the most important recommendation was that the Society should have an overall management committee or Council. Not until the closing weeks of 1845 did this proposal become effective* but the new Council lost no time in agreeing to petition for a Royal Charter. Tooke, as the Society's honorary solicitor, drafted the appropriate documents and saw proceedings through to grant. (The addition of 'Royal' to the Society's name did not take place until 1908.) In his *History of the Royal Society of Arts*, the former Secretary Henry Trueman Wood observed that:

> 'With the grant of a Royal Charter the first period of the Society's history may be held to have come to an end. After this it may be said to have entered on a new chapter of its existence. It found new aims and adopted novel methods; not only its constitution but its character was to a large extent altered, and with a reorganised system it may certainly be said to have started on a fresh career of usefulness.'[10]

Among the Webster committee recommendations which had the effect of altering the character of the Society was a proposal that the principal object of the Wednesday evening meetings should be the reading and discussion of communications on the arts and manufactures. It further suggested that, because the exclusion of patented inventions from awards had been extremely detrimental to the interests of the Society, regulations disqualifying patented inventions should be rescinded. This suggestion also was put into effect with little delay; *Transactions* for the period 1841–3 carried an Appendix of papers 'read before the Society at their Wednesday evening meetings ... including those relating to Patented Inventions, which were, until very recently, entirely prohibited from being

* Extracts from contemporary (1841–5) Minutes and Transactions of the Society of Arts are given in Appendix VIII.

brought before the Society in any shape whatever'.[11] Looking back on these events after rather more than a decade, Webster wrote of them:

> 'About the year 1840 the Society was in such a state of prostration and inanition, that its winding up and dissolution was actually proposed; this was successfully resisted by various alterations and reforms, which, after six or seven years, brought the Society into a state, the foundation of its present prosperity and usefulness. The admission and exhibition of inventions, though the subject of patents, was a leading instrument in the progress of resuscitation.' (See Appendix IX).

Another 'instrument in the progress of resuscitation' was the effort Webster and his associates put into introducing new members to the Society. Having regard to the business and professional connections of the principal recruiters, it followed that not only were many of their recruits technically-minded people but patent interests were strongly represented. As a consequence it seems likely that in the later 1840s a significant proportion of the Society's membership was sympathetic to patent reform, coinciding with a general revival of reform activity which initially had nothing to do with the Society.

The efforts of those who had worked for reform in the 1820s–30s had borne little fruit but the passing years had seen a great increase in the number of patents applied for. Grants were more than three times greater during the 1840s than the 1820s and their numbers continued to rise. Developments in mechanical devices and in the processes and machines to produce them made recourse to patents more frequent. However great the expense and the hazard involved in obtaining a patent it was often imperative that it should be done. Although secret working was sometimes resorted to, it was not a satisfactory option, especially in concerns employing more than a handful of people. Industrial espionage had long been a problem for innovators but, with the expansion of industry the increase in the size of many manufacturing units and the employment of large numbers of work-people, it had become an issue of ever-present concern to entrepreneurs seeking to keep ahead of competition.[12] As the century had progressed the patent systems of other countries – with their own failings, obstacles and advantages – had become increasingly of interest to British inventors. This increase in patent activity had, by the 1840s, brought forward a new profession, that of patent agent. No longer was the obtaining of patents principally in the hands of a few office-holders in departments of state with a slightly larger number of engineers and chemists preparing specifications as a side-line. In short, the patent scene of the 1840s was vastly different from that of the 1820s.[13]

Presentation of a petition to the House of Lords in 1847 on behalf of a newly-formed 'National Association for the Reform of the Patent Laws' seems to have been the first shot in a fresh campaign for reform. Other petitions followed from a motley collection of 'national' reform groups, from chambers of commerce and from committees established in industrial areas.[14] An interesting example of the latter was 'The Lambeth Patent Laws Reform Association' which, its prospectus stated, 'originated in the numerous cases brought before the South London Committee for the Exhibition of 1851, in which persons of limited means, desirous of availing themselves of the extraordinary publicity which will be afforded by the "Exhibition of Industry" were deterred by the heavy taxation imposed by the Patent Laws'. This committee and the petition it presented were very much a Maudslay, Son and Field affair. Joshua Field, CE, FRS, was the committee's chairman and Henry Maudslay [Jnr.] the treasurer. Established by Henry Maudslay [Snr.], the firm had taken over a 'green field site' in 1810. The works became a school for great engineers including Richard Roberts, Joseph Whitworth and James Nasmyth, all three of whom started manufactories in Manchester and all became members of the Society. (Joshua Field and several Maudslays were members.) Roberts and Whitworth were also members in 1836 of a British Association for the Advancement of Science committee on patent matters.

When the patent agent Hughes, taking advantage of the stimulation of interest in patent reform created by the prospect of the 1851 Exhibition, proposed a 'Manchester Patent Law Reform Association' Richard Roberts became that body's treasurer. For a chairman Hughes had approached a more senior member of the engineering profession, 'I solicited our respected and highly-honoured townsman, W. Fairbairn, Esq.,

C.E., to preside over the meeting [a public meeting arranged by Hughes], who consented in the most courteous manner.' After several meetings and the formation of a twenty-strong committee comprised principally of leading engineers and machinists, Hughes and two others drew up a memorial to be presented to the President of the Board of Trade. This document is remarkable for its moderation and also for closely foreshadowing the outcome of the campaign. After a flowery preamble in praise of the ingenuity of Englishmen and offering the opinion that 'every encouragement and security should be given to inventors, consistent with public welfare', it went on in a series of clauses to outline several failings in the existing system requiring remedy, including:

> 'The present very heavy expenses, loss of time, and other inconveniences occasioned by the intricate routine, or operation of passing through a great number of useless forms to which the inventor is subjected in obtaining "Letters Patent", exhibit a tendency not calculated to encourage, but absolutely to baffle and paralyze the efforts of a class so essential in maintaining the commercial pre-eminence of this kingdom.
>
> This class of persons should not, in obtaining Patent right for their inventions, be burthened with any more expenses than such as may be absolutely necessary for the establishment and maintenance of one government office, and for publishing full particulars of all patents granted.
>
> For want of an official record of patents, easy of access to the public, many patents are taken out for the same invention; ... we therefore beg humbly to suggest that there should be an easy means of ascertaining by an official record the full particulars of all patents granted, the dates of expired patents, and also the abandonment or forfeiture of unexpired ones.'[15]

It is unlikely that Hughes had difficulty persuading Fairbairn to chair his meetings for he was already on the committee of 'The Association of Patentees and Proprietors of Patents, for the Protection and Regulation of patent Property'. He had also been appointed a Commissioner for the 1851 Exhibition. Later he was to be a member of the Council of the Society of Arts. His membership of the Society dated from 1843 on the proposal of Charles Holtzapfel, mechanician, technical author, council member of ICE, chairman of the Society's Committee of

Mechanics, and active recruiter for the Society following publication of the Webster report. A year before Fairbairn, Robert Stephenson who was also to become a Council member had been recruited by John Bethell who, shortly afterwards, also proposed Richard Prosser, engineer of Birmingham. About the same time, Webster introduced Joseph Whitworth; Bennet Woodcroft, a textile engineer originating in Manchester and well-acquainted with Fairbairn; Benjamin Fothergill, another Manchester textile machinist; and John Scott Russell who was to become Secretary to the Society and was responsible for much of the preliminary work leading to the 1851 Exhibition.[16] An outstanding marine engineer, Russell was later to be responsible for the construction of the 'Great Eastern', using the Millwall shipyard earlier developed by Fairbairn and putting into practice many of the concepts relating to iron ship construction pioneered by Fairbairn.

Even before patent agent Hughes had brought his Manchester committee together, the Society of Arts had appointed its own committee on 'The Rights of Inventors', apparently at the suggestion of Henry Cole, recently introduced to the Society by Scott Russell. According to the preamble to its first printed report, this committee was to consider its subject 'in accordance with the principles agreed on by the council of the Society in 1849'.[17]

It was no coincidence that the Council turned its mind to patent reform at this time when it was heavily engaged with plans for exhibitions of manufactures. A small exhibition at the Society's house in 1846 had failed to meet the expectations of its devisors but one arranged the following year attracted 20,000 visitors. This success was improved upon in the two following years. Meanwhile, in March 1848, a deputation from the Society had waited upon the President of the Board of Trade to request government co-operation in organising more extensive displays and, consequent on a favourable response, the Society was able to make public the intention to proceed with much larger exhibitions at a more spacious venue. Even the small exhibitions of 1847, 8 and 9, must have raised questions in the minds of exhibitors (and might-have-been exhibitors reluctant to take the plunge) on the lines of 'If I put my most recent innovative products on display for all to see –

competitors as well as customers – what is to protect me from having my ideas copied?' Not surprisingly when the Society's patent reform committee issued its first report, it observed, 'Circumstances now connected with the Exhibition of the Works of Industry of all Nations, to take place in 1851, render the discussion of the question [of patent reform] inevitable.'[18]

'The principles agreed on by the council of the Society in 1849' when establishing its committee were:

1. That Inventors, Designers, etc. ought not to be subjected to any other expenses than such as may be absolutely necessary to secure to them the Protection of their Inventions.
2. That the difficulties and anomalies experienced in connexion with "Patents" should be removed.
3. That the present term of Copyright in Design for Articles of Manufacture, and the Protection afforded to the Authors and Proprietors of Inventions and of Designs in Arts and Manufactures, are inadequate.'[19]

To consider these 'principles' a balanced committee of more than a score of well-informed people was appointed. Heading the list was the Marquis of Northampton, President of the Royal Society, followed by the Earl of Radnor noted for his reforming activity. Another member prominent in other spheres was Milner Gibson, some-time President of the Board of Trade. Several other Members of Parliament were on the list. Manufactures, engineers, chemists and inventors were well represented along with people having no direct contact with industry. Henry Cole seems to have acted as secretary and to have prepared its reports. The first of these was printed in December 1850 and its initial paragraph provided an uncompromising description of the patent system as it then was:

> 'A British subject has no rights of property whatever in that intellectual labour which produces invention or scientific discovery, excepting such as he can obtain by petition from the Crown. He may have bestowed years of mental exertion and manual toil in perfecting a discovery most beneficial to mankind, still he is not in the position of being able to claim even the fruits of his labour as his own. He must become a petitioner for the right to

> the Crown, which is absolute and irresponsible ... By passing through a series of formulas, so antiquated that the origin of them is lost in the obscurity of past centuries – so numerous, that they can hardly be reckoned accurately – so intricate, that every one seems a pitfall to discourage scientific invention to the utmost – so inexplicable, that the utmost diversity of opinion obtains in interpreting them – so costly, as to place scientific intelligence wholly within the power of capital; an inventor may at last obtain a mere recognition of his right, which he is then at liberty to protect as he may be best able.'

Between establishment and publication of its first report the committee had been joined by someone whose contribution to its deliberations proved to be of less consequence than his ability to demonstrate the need for patent reform to a wider public than were the usual interested parties. Charles Dickens became a member of the Society in May 1850 soon after his return to England following prolonged periods spent abroad, including the USA where his 'novels sold in millions, for which he got not one halfpenny. To him this was of special importance, because upon an author's power to enjoy the fruits of his labour, to be paid for the pleasure he gave to his great public, rested the independence of the profession, it raised and deserved social status, its freedom from arrogant patronage.'[20]

Obviously Dickens could feel for the inventor who found problems in the way of receiving reward for the fruits of his labour. In addition his return to England had given him impetus to start something fresh and one new project to which he applied himself was *Household Words*, a periodical that first appeared in March 1850 and weekly thereafter. Its readership was intended to be Dickens' 'honest, English working man'. The spirit of *Household Words* is the spirit of reform. In the first issue was a plea for the removal of the newspaper tax; later issues followed with an attack on workhouse conditions, on lack of educational facilities, official failings related to a cholera outbreak and so on. A wonderful source of information on a system ripe for reform was provided in the Society's committee.

A RECITAL OF THE OFFICIAL STAGES, SO FAR AS THEY CAN BE MADE OUT, WHICH AN INVENTOR MUST UNDERGO IN OBTAINING LETTERS PATENT FOR AN INVENTION IN ENGLAND ONLY, PROVIDED HIS APPLICATION IS UNOPPOSED.

Stage		£ s d
1st.	Inventor prepares humble petition to the Crown,	
2d.	Which he must fortify by a declaration taken before a Master in Chancery, and pay	£0 1 6
3d.	He delivers petition and declaration to the Home Office, in Whitehall, and pays	2 2 6
4th.	Home Secretary signs petition after some days, and refers it to Attorney or Solicitor General	
5th.	Petition taken to the Attorney or Solicitor General, at their Chambers, and the fees paid to them and Clerks are	4 4 0
6th.	Attorney or Solicitor General reports in favour of petition, as a matter of course, unless opposed	
7th.	Report taken back to the Home Office, in Whitehall	
8th.	Home Office prepares a warrant, which echoes the report, and is	
9th.	Sent to the Queen to sign	
10th.	Returned to Home Office, and	7 18 6
11th.	Home Secretary countersigns warrant, and the fees paid are	
12th.	Warrant taken to Patent Office in Lincoln's Inn	
13th.	Clerk of the Patents prepares a draft of the Queen's bill and docquet of the bill, and the fees paid are	5 10 6
14th.	And engrosses two copies of bill, one for the Signet Office and one for the Privy Seal Office, fees	1 7 6
15th.	Stamp-duty on each	6 0 0
16th.	Engrossing Clerk of the Patent Office engrosses Queen's bill for signature, fees	1 1 0
17th.	Stamp for the same	1 10 0
18th.	Queen's bill taken to Attorney-General or Solicitor-General and signed by them, fees	6 0 0
19th.	Taken back to Home Secretary	
20th.	Sent by Home Secretary to the Queen	7 13 6
21st.	Signed by the Queen	
22d.	Returned to the Home Secretary, and the fees paid are	
23d.	Queen's bill taken to Signet Office, in Somerset House	
24th.	Clerk of the Signet prepares a signet bill for the Lord Keeper of the Privy Seal, and the fees paid are	4 7 0
25th.	Clerk of the Lord Keeper of the Privy Seal prepares a Privy Seal bill for the Lord Chancellor, and stamp; fees paid are	4 2 0
26th.	Privy Seal bill delivered to the Clerk of the Patents	
27th.	Clerk of the Patents engrosses the patent, and fees paid are	5 17 8
	Stamps for the patent, &c.	30 0 0
28th.	Clerk of the Patents prepares a docquet thereof	
29th.	Stamp for the docquet of patent	
30th.	Boxes for the patent	0 9 6
31st.	Fees to the deputy (?), the Lord Chancellor's Purse-bearer	2 2 0
32d.	Fees to the Clerk of the Hanaper	7 13 0
33d.	Fees to the Deputy Clerk of the Hanaper	0 10 0
34th.	Recipe of the Lord Chancellor for the Privy Seal bill, which he signs	1 11 6
35th.	Fees to the Deputy-Sealer and Deputy-Chaff Wax*	0 10 6
		£99 7 2

Exclusive of fees in cases of opposition and for enrolment of the specification.†

List of 'stages' in the patent-obtaining process as set out in the *First Report of the Society of Arts' Committee on the Rights of Inventors* (1850). This list was used by Dickens in his *Poor Man's Tale of a Patent*, of which the following is an extract 'I went through thirty-five stages. I began with the Queen upon the Throne. I ended with the Deputy Chaff-Wax. Note. I would like to see the Deputy Chaff-Wax. Is it a man or what is it?'

Dickens' record of the difficulties and costs besetting a would-be patentee is set in the framework of a tale of a poor man (an honest, English working man) who had 'been twenty years, off and on, completing an invention and perfecting it'. Coming fortuitously into a small inheritance he was persuaded to take out a patent. It proved to be an unhappy experience. 'I say nothing of being tired of my life, while I was patenting my invention. ... I went through 35 stages. I began with the Queen upon the throne, I ended with the Deputy Chaff-Wax. ... The whole gang of Hanapers and Chaff-Waxes must be done away with, England has been chaffed and waxed sufficient'.[21]

It is an entertaining tale; did it do more than amuse when it appeared in October 1850? Be that as it may, because it emanated from a respected source it made a useful contribution towards lifting the arcane subject of patents from being exclusively a matter for dissentient opinion in such specialist periodicals as *The Mechanics' Magazine* and *The Engineer* to the notice of a more general readership. Already, with meetings being organised and petitions being canvassed in so many industrial areas, local as well as national newspapers were venturing to mention a subject that would have received little attention twenty years earlier. For a variety of reasons, desirable and otherwise, patents were to provide news items throughout the next thirty years.

Although calls for reform now came from more numerous and more geographically widespread centres than during the 1820s and 30s and the number of petitions submitted was large, diversity of opinion with regard to the way forward was as great as ever. There now was, however, a realistic mood of compromise and an appreciation that change might have to be gradual. In spite of deep misgivings by some Right Honourable Members even the government was edging towards action, so that when patent agent Hughes supported by a couple of fellow-Mancunians attended on the President of the Board of Trade they were told that a Bill was in preparation. With the Great Exhibition only weeks away the Manchester men were impatient and distrusting and did not long delay before asking Brougham to draft a Bill. In this they had the co-operation of the Birmingham committee (where

Richard Prosser, a most useful member of the Society's committee, was prominent) and there was also input from the Society. Within days of Brougham introducing his draft a government Bill appeared.[22] Another Parliamentary Committee was appointed and, as in 1829, much evidence both oral and written, was taken. William Fairbairn represented Hughes' Manchester group before the committee, Henry Cole appeared for the Society of Arts and Thomas Webster supplied information on legal matters. The outcome was a proposal that a third Bill be prepared incorporating such material from the Brougham and government Bills as seemed likely to gain acceptance. This hybrid was hurriedly cobbled by Webster and, notwithstanding criticism from many directions, became law on the first of July, 1852.

The Patent Law Amendment Act, 1852 left much to be desired and much still to be worked for but it represented an enormous break with previous practices. With so many groups and so many able people possessed of specialist knowledge working towards a consensual end, all must share credit that something, however imperfect, was achieved. It transpired, however, that as a respected national body which for nearly a hundred years had been committed to encouraging innovation in manufactures and the practical arts, the Society was uniquely placed to play a leading role as the campaign for reform moved into a climacteric period and achieved its greatest success to date.

There was nothing transitory about the Society's reversal of attitude regarding patents for its continuing interest was significant in the further development of the patent system. At the first meeting of the 1852/3 Session Chairman of Council, Henry Cole, observed, 'The working of the new patent law will naturally receive the careful attention of the Council'. In the event, patents received almost continuous attention in the Society for more than thirty years to follow.[23] In his opening of session report, Cole went on to say that 'the Society has advocated the necessity of a national institution where patented inventions should be deposited and exhibited, and the value of such an establishment has been repeatedly shown by their annual exhibitions of recent inventions ... (Cole also hinted that these exhibitions might have a role in connection with a patent museum.) As early as 1848 the Council had caused an exhibition of inventions of the preceding twelve months – including patented inventions – to be organised[24] and such events were held annually for another fifteen years or so.

As if these and the exhibitions of industrial products that culminated with the major event of 1851 were not enough the Society was at the same time interesting itself in the education of artisans, an activity having little direct bearing on the Society's new approach to patents but which, nevertheless, was fortuitously to give rise to publicly expressed opinions on the subject.

A Rev. Dr. James Booth, possessed with a passionate devotion to the improvement of educational standards, was introduced to the Society in 1852 and immediately made a contribution of lasting value. It was he who proposed that the Society should have a weekly newspaper to be called the *Journal of the Society of Arts*.[25] As *Transactions* had suffered a hiccup in the 1840s resulting in its demise and as Booth had thought his proposal through in detail and could put it before Council in a form requiring minimum alteration, his suggestion was warmly welcomed and accepted. (The *Journal* soon proved to be a most valuable vehicle for providing information relating to patents through the publication of papers read on the subject and by providing a forum for discussion of the points they raised.) Bubbling with vigour and ideas, Booth was soon a member of Council and – for the 1855/6 session – Chairman. In giving the opening address of that session he expressed a view on an aspect of the Society's earlier activities that was to provoke a sharp response. Here is the sentence that raised hackles:

> 'During a period of our social history, when protection and monopoly were held by our most eminent statesmen and most expert statists to be the very tap roots of commercial prosperity and manufacturing industry, the Society of Arts discountenanced patents and monopolies of every kind.'

Using the correspondence column of the new *Journal* to 'observe' – 'as an old member of the Society' (a barbed shaft that) – Thomas Webster gave his view of the Society's former attitude to patents:

> 'It was a rule of the Society of Arts, in former days, that any invention the subject of a patent could not receive any pecuniary reward, it being considered that the patent was, or ought to be, the reward selected by the inventor himself, and that the funds of the society should be applied to the encouragement of those meritorious inventors who were prohibited by the cost of patents from securing to themselves property in the results of their own talents and ingenuity.'[26] (See Appendix IX for complete letter.)

It was in this letter that Webster went on to mention the improvement in the Society's affairs referred to earlier when he wrote of the reforms of the 1840s having 'brought the Society into a state, the foundation of its present prosperity and usefulness'. Six years later Webster's assessment was updated by the then Chairman of Council:

> 'In a career which now embraces the labours of more than a century, the Society has witnessed many vicissitudes, but although some of its original functions have been undertaken by kindred societies, yours is the only chartered body which seeks to promote manufactures and commerce by enlisting in their service science and art. By your union with Mechanics, and other Institutions, and by the encouragement you have afforded to the systematic instruction of adults, you have lengthened your cords and strengthened your stakes. The number of your members has doubled in the last ten, and quadrupled in the last fifteen years. The last Session witnessed the election of 548 new members, and the council has had this evening the gratification of notifying the proposal of 306 candidates for election, being nearly thrice the number ever submitted for election at a single sitting. These are proofs that the Society continues to enjoy the sympathy, confidence, and esteem of the public.'[27]

This passage records a singular turn-around in the space of less than twenty years. The Society was no longer primarily a premium-offering body keeping patents at arm's length but was busy supporting and encouraging the practical arts in a variety of new ways,[28] including a continuing active interest in the patent system which also had changed dramatically due in large part to the influence of the Society. On the evidence available there seems little doubt that Webster and his associates (including a high proportion of members with patent interests) had saved the Society from an untimely end and in so doing had created a situation in which it was able to take a leading role when the patent reform movement's digitate groups were again gathering themselves for yet another assault on an out-dated relic of medieval court procedures.

Thomas Webster, Q.C.

5

'A blue-coated Encyclopaedia of Human Progress'

While the 1852 Act pleased no one it had the merit of satisfying even the most radical reformers that a start had been made. Perhaps patent agent Hughes' Manchester group had most cause for satisfaction. It had been modest in setting out desirable requirements and these were in great measure met. Applicants should not, they said, 'be burthened with any more expenses than such as may be absolutely necessary for the establishment and maintenance of one government office,' also 'there should be an easy means of ascertaining by an official record the full particulars of all patents granted [and] the dates of expired patents.' Whether they regarded the fees set in pursuance of the Act as falling within desired requirements is doubtful. There was manifestly a two-way split on this aspect of patent reform (as no doubt on many others) in Manchester where the Chamber of Commerce expressed the view in 1851 that

> 'If the cost be made cheap, every trifling improvement, in every process of manufacture, would be secured by a patent; in a few years no man would be able to make such improvements on his machinery or processes as his own experience may suggest without infringing upon some other person's patent: useless litigation would follow.'[1]

The fees set down in 1852 were, in fact, slightly higher than had previously been required for an English patent. However, they were in respect of grants covering the entire United Kingdom, henceforth inventors no longer had to weigh up the likely need for additional protection in Scotland and/or Ireland.

There was to be one patent office for the whole of the United Kingdom, although the prospect of housing petition-receiving and patent-sealing officials under the same roof as the staff who would have the duty of receiving, indexing and publishing specifications caused grave disquiet among some people. This novel bipartite organisation was to be under the control of 'Commissioners of Patents' comprising the Lord Chancellor, the Master of the Rolls and the Law Officers of England and Wales, Scotland and Ireland. In practice, only the English Law Officers performed the duties of 'Commissioners' and, as years passed, 'the Commissioners' were usually the Master of the Rolls and the Attorney and Solicitor Generals. By the penultimate day of 1852 accommodation had been found for the fledgling department of state in ground floor rooms of an old building off Chancery Lane recently vacated by members of the Lord Chancellor's department for whom more spacious accommodation had been prepared.

Before the new Patent Office had begun its task of publishing 'full particulars of all patents granted', the Society of Arts had started to provide this kind of information itself. In the first issue of the *Journal* (26th November 1852) were particulars of recent patent applications and of patents sealed, information that was provided weekly thereafter. The Society was obviously pleased with itself:

> 'It cannot fail to be a matter of congratulation to members of the Society, that the labours of their Committee for the improvement of the Patent Laws have met with such signal success; the greater part of the principles advocated by that Committee having been adopted by the legislature. It is hoped the Commissioners will lose no time in preparing for public use (as they are directed by the Act) a complete Index of all past Patents.'[2]

The Society and the public had not long to wait for news from the Commissioners' Office of an Index. In less than three months from the appearance of the Society's first *Journal*, Royal Assent was granted for an Act 'to provide for the Purchase for the public Use of certain Indexes of

Specifications'. The Act explained, 'whereas it would require some Years to make Indexes thereof [1,500 and upwards specifications] on a proper Arrangement and Classification: And whereas Mr. Bennet Woodcroft has already made complete Indexes of such Specifications, which the Commissioners have examined and approved of, ... it is expedient that such Indexes be purchased for the Use of the Public.'[3]

A great many specification indexes must have been available at this time (though often incomplete) because patent agents had been compiling lists for their own purposes over many years. This they were able to do during the normal course of their professional activities in which they often were required to make searches through official records on behalf of clients in hope of discovering the state of the prior art in a client's chosen field. Such information was highly desirable in order adequately to distinguish the old from that which the client believed to be new and to avoid the expense of applying for a patent in respect of something on which a prior grant had been made.

Bennet Woodcroft, whose indexes were to be officially published, appears to have gone well beyond others in this field. It would seem that he had somehow obtained from the Lord Chancellor's department a list of all patents granted from 1617. Although the list was not complete omissions were few; it should also be remembered that the 1617 grant – Woodcroft's 'No.1' – was not the first English invention patent. Equipped with the official list the patent rolls could be searched; no easy operation because invention patents were not in any way separated from other enrolled grants of privileges, such as titles, charters, land bequests and so on. Woodcroft did not lack financial resources and it is clear that he must have employed others to carry out such an extensive and tedious task and then compile indexes based on the information retrieved. In addition to presenting the material in three distinct forms, i.e. an alphabetical index of inventors' names and chronological and subject-matter indexes, a further volume was prepared indicating the office in which every enrolled specification was to be found with notes on books, journals and other documents in which law proceedings and other matters relating to the inventions were mentioned.[4]

Woodcroft differed from most patent reformers – and from Webster in particular, notwithstanding his 'Thomas Webster is my friend' in a letter to the Society – in holding a limited view of the changes necessary to the patent system. For him the only essential requirement was that readily accessible information on past and current inventions should be provided. It mattered little to him that the application procedures were expensive, cumbersome and time-consuming; examination of specifications he considered unnecessary, being of opinion that inventors ought to have means available allowing them to carry out their own investigations and – by so doing – avoid the trouble and expense of proceeding further with a fruitless venture.

Bitter experiences as an inventor and patentee had shaped Woodcroft's outlook. In giving evidence before the 1851 Select Committee he was able to express some of the frustration experienced by those who had traversed the labyrinthine ways of the patent-seeking process:

> 'There is one great evil I found to exist, namely, that the specifications are enrolled in three different offices; the Rolls Chapel, the Enrolment Office, and the Petty Bag Office, and at none of them had they a complete index of all the enrolled Specifications of Patents; so that, when an enquirer asks for a certain Specification, they will look in their index which contains the Specifications only which have been enrolled there; and if they have not got the Specification asked for, they will tell him, "We have no such enrolled Specification, you must go elsewhere"; then they say, "But you must nevertheless pay your fee for the search; that is necessary"; then he goes to the next office; if they have it not there the fee for the search is again demanded. He then goes to the third office, and it may not even be there as the Specification may not have been enrolled. So that the enquirer not only loses his time in running to all the three offices, but he is compelled to pay three separate fees.' 'Weeks were often occupied in the task, and from £2–£3 have been paid by a single inventor in one day for searches at the Petty Bag Office alone'.[5]

A member of the Society of Arts from the early days of 1845, following proposal by Thomas Webster, Woodcroft had participated from the first in the work of the Society's committees including those leading to the 1851 Exhibition. As would be expected he was also active on the Committee on the Rights of Inventors, being already engaged in the patent reform movement generally and in conducting minor campaigns of his own principally directed at those defects of the system mentioned in the quotation immediately above.

Following the 1852 enactment Woodcroft was soon in a position to put right those defects he perceived most clearly and which he opposed so trenchantly. In what manner the choice was made when he was appointed head of the specification division of the new Patent Office is not known, but it is inconceivable that the Commissioners of Patents could have selected a more suitable person for the post. It was as if his previous life had uniquely prepared him for this position and he applied himself to the formidable tasks he faced with remarkable vigour and zeal. A tribute by his principal memorialist was wholly fitting: 'Mr. Woodcroft was no ordinary Government official, and, being unfettered by any tradition of routine, he set himself, immediately on his appointment, to carry out the Act not in the spirit of doing as little as he must, but as much as he could'.[6]

As seen by historians of the Patent Office 'the Indefatigable Mr. Woodcroft' as *Household Words* referred to him, is a remarkable founding father, which indeed he was. As seen from a Society of Arts viewpoint, he was a member effective in putting into practice objectives discussed and pressed for by the Society, howbeit in his own idiosyncratic manner. The extent to which Woodcroft was committed to patent reform before joining the Society is unclear. Certainly he desired improved facilities for inventors but through the 1840s he had many irons in his fire among which development and promotion of his marine propulsion inventions were paramount. Nevertheless, once enrolled with the Society he quickly became a very active member and his work on committees of the Society brought him to the notice of people whose influences probably had a bearing on his appointment to the new Office.

Woodcroft's enthusiasm for improved facilities for inventors carried him well beyond the requirements of the Act. Left very much to his own devices by the Patent Commissioners, he not only brought about speedy printing of current specifications as the Act laid down but simultaneously embarked on the task of copying from patent rolls all specifications (including their drawings, which had not only to be copied with precision but also re-drawn on lithographic stones for printing) from the year 1617. By 1860 printed copies of any specification from the earlier to the later date were available for the cost of paper and printing. 'Thus it is that Britain possesses this magnificent unsurpassed printed record of patents of invention – this "blue-coated encyclopaedia of human progress"'.[7] (Each printed specification was supplied in a blue paper cover.)

This great publishing achievement has been well described elsewhere but nowhere has it been remarked upon with more verve than in *Household Words*.[8] As well as describing in highly favourable terms the printed output, *Household Words* went on to commend as 'one of the best features of the proceedings of the Commissioners' the 'presentation of copies of all their publications ... to the principal towns in the UK, to be placed in such public free libraries as now exist, or may hereafter be formed ... This excellent gift has in numerous instances laid the foundation of public free-libraries where none previously existed. In some of the towns there have been held Industrial

Exhibitions of the lithographic drawings relating to the several patents on one particular subject; while foremen and workmen from factories are often to be seen busily poring over the books and drawings in the free libraries'. *Household Words* was obviously taking its cue from the Commissioners' Report for 1856 which would contain a measure of Woodcroft input. There may also have been a more direct contribution from him, he was a born propagandist for his own activities and not beyond a little exaggeration. However, such encouragement to learning among artisans and workmen as here referred to would go down well at the Society of Arts.

Even as *Household Words* was offering such warm approval of his work, Woodcroft was launching another important innovation by initiating a series of classified abridgment volumes as a further aid, as he saw it, to avoiding misapplication of time and labour in re-inventing what was already known. Early abridgment volumes contained lists of libraries and other institutions at which the Commissioners' publications could be perused. According to these lists, abridgment volumes were available in nearly 300 Mechanics' Institutions and Working Men's Clubs.

A much shorter list of 'towns' to which complete sets of the printed output of Woodcroft's department were supplied contained some quite fascinating entries: Between 'Belfast (Queen's College) and York (Lower Council Chamber, Guildhall)' came 'London (British Museum; Society of Arts John Street, Adelphi)' and some more unlikely repositories, such as, 'Crewe (Railway Station)' and 'Gorton (Railway Station)'. (Crewe and Gorton, were homes to major locomotive and related depots staffed by large numbers of manual workers resident within compact areas.) As with the 'Macclesfield Useful Knowledge Society' and other such groups listed, the object was to make technical literature available to working men. Woodcroft was a serious devotee of the 'self-help' school, as was his friend William Fairbairn with whom he had in his Manchester days planned but never put into effect a periodical to be called *The Workshop*.

As would be expected, all the Commissioners' publications could also be consulted at their office where a small reading room had been provided. *Household Words* had a paragraph about this small room. 'The building once occupied by the

Masters in Chancery, is now placed at the disposal of the Commissioners of Patents. One among the many rooms in this building is now a reading room. ... A small room it is: much too small indeed: but it is the beginning of a good thing, its gradual growth may be pleasantly watched hereafter'. That 'gradual growth' led to the elementary reading room becoming one of the foremost scientific and technical libraries of the world. Its very growth and success contributed to its dissociation from its parent office to form the core of the British Library's Science, Technology and Innovation Division.

To the Commissioners' publications in their reading-room, Woodcroft added his personal collection of books, journals and like material of a technical nature as the nucleus of a Patent Office Library. (Included in this collection were volumes of *Transactions of the Society of Arts.* In what was probably his first communication with the Society's Secretary very soon after his election, Woodcroft had requested that a full set of the *Transactions* be forwarded to him.) A larger and more valuable addition to the Library came from Richard Prosser comprising some 700 titles (Woodcroft's contribution was of about 400 works.) Prosser, a Birmingham engineer and patentee, had joined the Society shortly before Woodcroft, i.e. in 1843. He was equally zealous for patent reform and served on the Society's Committee for Legislative Rights where his contribution was great, one of his suggestions being of especial significance. An issue to which the Committee gave attention was how 'invention' was to be defined. It had before it a form of words attributed to Chief Justice Jervis (as he was in 1851) prepared for an abortive Bill of 1833. Long and detailed, it would probably have given rise to many a field-day of legal argument had it been adopted. Nevertheless, it appears from the Committee's first report that some of its members leaned to it.[9] Happily, Prosser pressed for and gained acceptance of the brief definition to be found in the Statute of Monopolies of 1624, in essence 'any manner of new manufacture'.[10] The Courts were already well versed in interpretation of this phrase and continued with care and skill to mark its boundaries through more than a century and a half of shifting tides of scientific and technical development.

From the Society's earliest days it had required full disclosure of subjects granted its awards. Where possible this involved deposit of a model or of a full-scale device in its Repository where the public was free to view and copy. As has already been noted, in the 1840s the Society also began a series of exhibitions of new inventions open to all who cared to exhibit or to visit. Under the date 6 December 1848 *Transactions* set out a General Notice for such an exhibition: 'The Council proposes to make a collection of Models of new and important improvements in Mechanics, to form an Exhibition ... The Council requests the loan of Models for that purpose.' Following his statement 'the working of the new Patent Law will naturally receive the careful attention of the Council' in his 1852 Chairman's address, Henry Cole went on to say 'the Society have advocated the necessity of a national institution where patented inventions should be deposited and exhibited and the value of such an establishment has been repeatedly shown by their annual exhibition of recent inventions'.[11]

Cole's words had an echo in the *Third Report of the Commissioners of the Exhibition of 1851* (at page 35) in which there was recorded a proposal to appoint a committee 'to consider the best mode of aiding in establishing a Museum of Inventions.' Bennet Woodcroft was among several Society members named to join this body. He already possessed a small collection of models. Some of these he had no doubt acquired because he was an inveterate collector; some as visual aids when giving discourses on machines at University College, London. For whatever reason acquired they fitted into the didactic element in his 'self-help' notions. He appreciated that practical men of his time were usually less at ease with written descriptions or even drawings, than they were when inspecting a machine or model. These could also be used as an encouragement to further development on the lines, 'Look chaps, this is what other fellows have done, can you not now do better?'

It was fortuitous for Woodcroft (and for the history of technology) that a 'Museum of Inventions' had great appeal for the Prince Consort who lost little time in summoning Woodcroft to discuss the suggestion when put forward by the Commissioners of the Exhibition and backed by the Society. Woodcroft in turn lost no time in canvassing support (and

The Science Museum's humble origin
Woodcroft's insistence that entrance to his collection of industrial artifacts should be free brought him into conflict with Henry Cole of the Science and Art Department, resulting in the Woodcroft collection being cramped into an iron shed beside the Department's more spacious premises. *Reproduced by kind permission of the Science Museum, London. (Image reference number 820/78 copyright protected.)*

hardware) throughout industrial areas. Against Woodcroft's wishes but in keeping with those of the Prince the 'Patent Museum' was set up in South Kensington, an arrangement to which Woodcroft was never reconciled. Notwithstanding this disappointment he threw himself into collecting technical artifacts with enthusiasm and, although his museum lacked space and was a terrible clutter, it housed many important objects which might otherwise have been lost. By 1885 the 'Patent Museum' had passed under the control of the Department of Science and Art and a report of that year hints at the value for historians of industrial technology of much of Woodcroft's collection, which was to form a basis for the present national Science Museum:

> 'The Patent Museum contains objects illustrating steps in the history of mechanical inventions, and contrivances of importance and interest, without regard to whether they have been patented or not. Among these, for example, are the earliest locomotive and stationary steam engines; the first engine used in steam navigation; the first reaping machine; Arkwright's original spinning machinery; all Sir Charles Wheatstone's original apparatus, showing a complete history of the various steps by which he perfected electric telegraphy; many of Edison's original electrical inventions; some old clocks dating from 1325; and other objects of similar interest.'[12]

As if a publishing house, a library and a museum were not enough, the Commissioners of Patents found they had to take on an art gallery as well. A communication from the Prince Consort to the Society of Arts in December, 1853 intimated that the Prince had received a suggestion that an exhibition of portraits of inventors was desirable. Such an exhibition was, of course, desirable to inventor Woodcroft who embellished the title page of one of his publications with a quotation: 'Upon every invention of value we erect a statue to the inventor, and give him a liberal honourable reward'. Respectful to its royal President, the Society announced that it had started a collection of portraits and at a meeting to discuss the Patent Laws on 1st February, 1854 the walls of the Great Room were appropriately adorned with inventors' likenesses. Woodcroft was as zealous in collecting for the 'Gallery of Inventors' as he was for the 'Museum of Inventions'. The portraits soon joined the museum objects at South Kensington.[13]

The library associated with the Patent Office which Woodcroft was so prompt in creating had been on the Society's agenda, as was a museum of inventions – favoured also by the Commissioners of the Great Exhibition and the Prince Consort. The Gallery of Portraits of Inventors may have been Woodcroft's idea but its formation was in the first place dependent on his having the ear of Prince Albert – through their joint association with the Society – and then on publicity provided by the Society's *Journal* and display in the Society's House. In short, although Woodcroft achieved a very great deal much of his success derived from earlier Society debates or from initial Society backing.*

As previously indicated, on matters of patent reform Woodcroft's outlook was more limited than that of many members of the Society. He seemed quite unable to grasp that the improvements consequent on the 1852 Act were insufficient and that there was more to be done, much more. Those who laboured on in pressing for additional alterations to the system could not expect and did not receive encouragement or assistance from him.

* Appendix X relates to the 'Patent Museum', the 'Gallery of Inventors' and thoughts on them by the Prince Consort, the Society of Arts and Bennet Woodcroft. Appendix XI also refers to these subjects.

6

'... heard great argument about it and about: but evermore came out by the same door wherein they went'

Giving evidence before a parliamentary committee in 1871, William Carpmael observed that the 1852 Act had provided a 'very substantial improvement' over previous practice. This was praise indeed from someone who had been well satisfied with the old ways and had set his face against reform. There had been others also, though probably few in number, who had been content to leave things as they were. Notwithstanding that some of them – like William Carpmael – could acknowledge the improvements flowing from the Act, they saw no cause for further changes. To this cluster of 'Contents' were added many who had formerly been dissatisfied but considered the amendments effected to be adequate. Some old campaigners were only too aware however that much still waited to be done, for them what had been enacted was only a beginning.

Although the nature of further improvements and the most desirable ways of effecting them continued to be discussed with little consensus, a collateral controversy provided an additional hindrance to progress. From early in the nineteenth century (and, indeed, long before) a variety of arguments had been put forward for the total abolition of patents. Behind some of these adverse attitudes to patents may have lain notions that it was beyond the wit of man to remedy something so archaic and unsuited to its purpose, but even a perfectly managed patent system would have been unacceptable to other contenders for abolition. By the 1860s those opposing patents on ideological grounds had become more numerous, more vocal and more influential. Patents, according to one influential group, imposed a restraint on freedom of trade and, as the free trade movement gained ground, calls for the abolition of patents increased. Independent from but often expressed in conjunction with free trade principles was a doctrine of natural evolution in the field of technology. 'The seeds of invention exist, as it were, in the air, ready to germinate whenever suitable conditions arise, and no legislative interference is needed to ensure their growth in proper season', declared Sir William Armstrong.[1] 'Nearly all useful inventions depend less on any individual than on the progress of society. A want is felt ... ingenuity is directed to supply it; and the consequence is, that a great number of suggestions or inventions of similar kind come to light ... Thus the want suggests the invention, and ... the State should not reward him who might be lucky enough to be the first to hit on the thing required.'[2]

The last quotation, taken from *The Economist* of 26 July, 1851,* epitomizes utterances of John Lewis Ricardo the 'principal advocate of reform or abolition of the patent system' in the House of Commons until his death in 1862. His place was taken by Robert Andrew Macfie, a Liverpool sugar refiner, who made innumerable speeches in the Commons and elsewhere (including the Society of Arts) in opposition to patents, and published several books on the subject including *The Patent Question under Free Trade*. *The Economist* was a ready vehicle for the propagation of anti-patent views. An editorial of 1850 included:

> 'Before ... [the inventors] can ... establish a right of property in their inventions, they ought to give up all the knowledge and assistance they have derived from the knowledge and inventions of others. ... Their inventions are, in fact, parts of the great mental whole of society, and they have no right of property in their inventions.'[3]

As would be expected of an impartial body providing a forum for free discussion of a wide range of topics, all aspects of the patent issue received an airing in the Society's House. Although many evenings were devoted specifically to the

* *The Times* also joined in the patent debate in 1851, see Appendix XII.

subject, it did not require a pre-arranged debate to bring out expressions of opinion. One such situation arose in 1853 when applications for the Society's premiums were under assessment. A Mr. Denison, having displayed and described a lock of his devising, stated that the lock was not patented 'as he agrees with many eminent persons who consider patents an obstruction to science'. Whereupon, 'Mr. Winkworth referred to the principle of Patents, to which he entirely objected, but did not feel at liberty to open up the question.' Notwithstanding Mr. Winkworth's reservations, John Scott Russell chairing the meeting felt obliged to bring out the penitence stool: 'The Chairman said in regard to the Patent Laws he must plead guilty to being the owner of two or three patents; but he fully agreed with Lord Glanville, the Philosophical Jury of the Great Exhibition, Colonel Sir William Reid, Sir William Cubbitt, Mr. Brunel, Mr. Winkworth, Mr. Denison, and other gentlemen who had been named, that it would be an advantage to the ingenuity of this and every other country if all property in patents were annihilated; and he believed that such a consummation was rapidly approaching.'[4]

However clear it was to John Scott Russell and others of like mind that the consummation so devoutly desired was at hand, changes in UK patent practices move slowly – which may be to their eventual good. It merits noting here that there was nothing peculiarly British about the pro/anti-patent controversy. It was Europe-wide and some countries came close to 'annihilating' their patent systems, though only the Netherlands went the whole way by abrogating its patent laws; only to make a fresh start many years later. In the UK a programme of abolition would have been difficult to carry through; notwithstanding its manifest defects, the system had survived for three centuries and something more than respect for old institutions kept it alive. Not least among the causes of its continued existence was that the inventing public, far from turning its back on it, was making more use of it year by year. In the decade 1740–49 the number of patents granted was 74, fifty years later – 1790–99 – it had risen to 643, and in the period 1840–49 it was 4,570. From 1855 to 1870 grants ran at about 2,000 **annually**, followed by a rising curve through later decades.

It will be seen from the considerable increase in grants consequent on the 1852 Act becoming operative that the improvements it introduced were appreciated. But little more than a year from the Act taking effect a discussion took place at the Society's House on 'Defects in the Administration of the Patent Laws'.[5] This was the first of many such considerations; early volumes of the *Journal* are liberally sprinkled with references to patents. As Henry Cole had said, 'The working of the new patent law will naturally receive the careful attention of the Council'.

In his *History of the Royal Society of Arts*, Trueman Wood rather surprisingly suggested that the Society displayed little interest in patents for many years following the 1852 enactment: 'After the passing of the Patent Law Amendment Act of 1852, a measure which ... owed a great deal to the Society of Arts, the question of Patent Law reform was for a long time allowed to slumber, so far as the Society was concerned. The Act was working extremely well, and the criticisms of objectors were mainly directed to matters of detail, which might well have been dealt with by administrative rather than legislative reform.'[6] True, there was no activity in the Society for more than twenty five years comparable to that associated with the 1849/51 'Rights of Inventors' committee and related moves directed to putting pressure on the government but men like Fairbairn and Webster neither slumbered nor slept during that time. Over those years many societies and groups pushed hard for further reforms and many members of the Society of Arts were far from idle in the patent cause even though the Society was not launching major initiatives.

Pressure from many quarters induced the government to set up a Royal Commission which sat through 1863 and much of 1864 receiving written evidence from and hearing a vast array of witnesses, including Thomas Webster and John Scott Russell. William Fairbairn was a Commissioner.[7] Much consideration was given to the way in which patent matters were handled by the courts and how the number of patents that were bad for want of novelty and/or lacking an adequate description could be reduced. A great many such patents, the Commission reported, were 'employed by the patentees only to embarrass manufacturers'. As expressed in the minority report of W.M. Hindmarch, QC, 'Specifications of inventions are frequently prepared in such a manner as to occasion great difficulty in construing them ... There is too much reason for believing that specifications are thus prepared with a fraudulent object'.

Among many other matters, Hindmarch recommended that specifications should have to define with precision the inventions to which they related and that sufficiency of definition 'should be ascertained and certified by competent persons appointed to perform that duty'. Although those 'competent persons' would carry out a limited form of examination, Hindmarch did not favour any inquiry into novelty. Here he differed from Webster who argued for an official, though limited, novelty search. Many witnesses were against examination of any kind; others, including Scott Russell, favoured strict examination. This question of examination was long to remain a stumbling block. Those against could marshal many reasons for their view. Those in favour displayed such a range of views as to how extensive or limited examination ought to be as must have run the whole gamut of possibilities. Then, similarly, there were as many differing opinions on the form of structure required to effect examination; non-specialist judges sitting with scientific or technical experts highly esteemed in their professions; specialist judges with or without lay assessors; panels of judges or single judges; a right of appeal or no appeal; the permutations were great. So it was with every issue falling within the purview of the 1863 Commissioners. As in 1829 there was opinion in plenty that much needed to be improved and little consensus on how it was to be achieved. Woodcroft, having obtained all he considered desirable in 1852, remained contentedly conservative through this and succeeding inquiries; provide the public with facilities to carry out their own searches and then let applicants look to themselves was his consistent line.

Much was expected of this Commission and hopes were high in many quarters. C.D. Abel, consulting engineer and patent agent wrote shortly before the Commission reported:

> 'The consideration of the existing Patent Laws, with a view to amending them ... has of late greatly occupied the minds of

> most persons connected with the industrial Arts and Manufactures ... and the result has been that the Commissioners appointed by Parliament early last Session to inquire into this important question have been enabled to collect a vast amount of information from all quarters. There is, therefore, great hope that their Report, together with a Bill embodying their recommendations, will shortly be laid before Parliament, with every prospect of the latter becoming law this Session.'[8]

Compare then an opinion shortly following publication of the Commissioners' Report:

> 'Composed of men thoroughly experienced in the working of these [patent] laws, presided over by Lord Stanley, whose acquired knowledge on this subject is as sound and comprehensive as that of any practical lawyer, and who, at various times, has published several valuable suggestions for the improvement of these laws, that Commission seemed pre-eminently qualified to discharge the duties entrusted to it. Unhappily, the result falls short of the most reasonable anticipations. The individual opinion of any member of the Commission would have been more valuable than the Report which it has issued.'[9]

The Commissioners themselves do not appear to have been happy with the outcome of their deliberations. The final paragraph of the majority Report gave few grounds for cheer – or hope:

> 'While, in the judgment of the Commissioners, the changes suggested will do something to mitigate the inconveniences now generally complained of by the public as incident to the working of the Patent Law, it is their opinion that these inconveniences cannot be wholly removed. They are in their belief inherent in the nature of a Patent Law, and must be considered as the price which the public consents to pay for the existence of such a law.'

Not only did the Commissioners' inquiry do little positive good for the patent system but it had at least one negative effect. It seems to have been effective in bringing about a change in the views of the Chairman – hitherto favourable to patents – for in a House of Commons speech some time later he set out his objections to 'the principle of patents'.[10]

Most of the recommendations of the Commission required legislation which was never carried through but there were also matters that were not put into effect for which administrative action alone would have been necessary. With regard to matters bearing on the Patent Office the patent agent Charles Abel painted a depressing picture. After generous words of praise for 'the very able Superintendent of Specifications, Mr. Bennet Woodcroft, through whose exertions' much had been achieved, he continued:

> 'It is however greatly to be regretted, and is indeed a fact hardly to be accounted for, that whilst there has accumulated a sum of £220,000 in the hands of the Commissioners [of Patents], which sum was available for the building of "proper Places or Buildings for an Office or Offices for the purpose of this [the 1852] Act", and generally to other reasonable requirements of the Patent Office, and whilst such surplus is still increasing to the extent of £40,000 annually, the efforts of Mr. Woodcroft to supply the public with perfect means of acquainting itself in the easiest possible manner with the nature of all patented Inventions have been crippled and hindered through want of an ample and complete Patent Office, etc., as well as the want of an adequate Staff of educated and competent persons for the purpose.
>
> It is self-evident that the Indices and Abridgments of patented Inventions, unless perfect and reliable in the information they profess to give, can be practically of little avail to the inquiring Inventor. If there be omitted the enumeration of but one Invention, if but one Specification be imperfectly abridged, or the nature of the subject-matter be misrepresented, then just that very omitted or misconstrued Invention may be the one, the pre-existence of which it is of the utmost importance to the Inventor to ascertain. Unfortunately neither the Indices nor the Abridgments are perfect in this respect. ... The public can hardly be aware that the extremely difficult and delicate matter of drawing the Abridgments of Specifications, involving as it does the correct appreciation and extraction of the essence of the Invention from a long and, in many cases, very confused description of the same, is performed **by contract at the rate of seven shillings each**, being in many cases not so much as a law-

clerk would charge for copying them, without understanding a word.'

Charles Abel went on to deplore the accommodation provided for the library – 'huddled together in two or three small passages and rooms' and where printed specifications were 'situated in a portion of a narrow and semi-obscure passage (partly lit by gas), where crowds of eager searchers are continually jostling against each other'. 'Every one who comes in contact with the details of the Patent Office for the first time exclaims that it is being starved, or that it is a disgrace to the Nation'. Referring again to the 'surplus fund in the hands of the Commissioners' of £220,000 he pointed out the obvious, 'and yet the new Patent Office **is not commenced**.'[11]

In spite of criticisms being repeated time and again through the 1860s and 70s of the Patent Office, its ways, works and cramped accommodation, by bodies that ought to have been able to exert more influence than one patent agent, nothing of any great substance was done to improve matters. So far as buildings were concerned (some other causes of complaint received earlier attention), remedies were long delayed. In reporting a Commons debate in 1891 *The Times* stated that a member of the government had 'examined thoroughly the buildings in which the work of the Patent Office was done, and any more inconvenient buildings both for the gentlemen employed and the public he has never seen'. A less distinguished and more transient periodical risked a prediction in 1898: 'After holding the distinction of occupying the dingiest, dirtiest and most ill-suited building in London for a number of years, the Patent Office is at last to be pulled down'. Half a century after the 1852 enactment the statutory provision regarding 'proper Places or Buildings for an Office or Offices' was being acted upon. Construction of a final planned wing was adjourned in 1912 never to be completed.[12]

How could it be that with general acknowledgement that much was required to improve the facilities provided by and for the Patent Office that little or nothing was done for so long? Why, within a couple of years of Charles Abel, William Hindmarch and others stressing the importance of accurate indexes and abridgments was there a Direction from the

Commissioners of Patents that applicants should prepare their own abridgments[13] – in spite of it being widely accepted that many specifications were ill-prepared? Then, ten years later, when the failings of this Direction were only too apparent, was the previous system of 'contract' abridgments restored with the former 'contract price' halved from a rate of pay ridiculed in 1864 by Abel for being too low? What were the Commissioners of Patents doing to allow matters generally considered to be unsatisfactory to worsen for more than two decades? And what was Woodcroft, one time patent reformer, doing to allow his concept of accurate indexes and abridgments to lapse deplorably? In 1852 it had seemed as reasonable as it was obvious that the high legal officers of state who for centuries had held principal responsibility for patent grants and records – the Lord Chancellor, the English Law Officers and their Scottish and Irish equivalents, and the Master of the Rolls – should continue to exercise overall control of the up-dated system. In retrospect the flaws of the arrangement are manifest. Of the eight Commissioners appointed (four of whom never acted), seven came and went with every change of government. In the 1850–70 period, for example, prime ministers snaked in and out of office like yo-yos, consequently some of the legal officers following in their trains served very brief apprenticeships. The principal duties of these parliamentary gentlemen in no way related to patents and at best they only met as Commissioners twice yearly. (In at least one year they did not achieve that modest target.) The one Commissioner who did not change office with government changes was the Master of the Rolls who, again, possessed no specialist patent knowledge, had judicial functions to perform and, following the 1838 Public Records Act, had duties relating to the newly-established (and newly-built) Public Records Office to fill any of his spare time. Add to this that most of the Commissioners tended towards being antipathetic to patents and one sees that a board of directors more inimical to the prosperity and progress of the organisation they were appointed to control could hardly have been devised.

After naming the eight legal functionaries as Commissioners, Section 1 of the 1852 Act goes on – 'together with such other person or persons as may from time to time be appointed'.

Suggestions that this component of the Act be instituted were repeatedly put forward over thirty years without satisfactory result. Not atypical of responses was a Bill introduced in 1879 in which it was proposed that there be five additional Commissioners, the intention being, it would appear, that they should be people with scientific or technical interests. However, although the legally-qualified Commissioners would continue to be paid, no payment for the additional five was envisaged. It need hardly be mentioned that that proposal was a non-starter.

An observation by Thomas Webster to a House of Commons Committee of Inquiry in 1864 throws a curious light on the Commissioners' mode of operating. In the course of a discussion in which Webster mentioned the lack of office accommodation for effecting full implementation of the Act, a Committee member referred to the 'Clerk of the Commissioners'. Webster responded, 'He has no proper office; the Clerk of the Commissioners is supposed, in fact, to be the Commission; and by the return made to the House, it would appear that he really is the Commission. I observe he said in the return, that there were very few meetings, and that they were unnecessary, because he was in constant communication with them. He has no room'. Brought back to the position of the 'Clerk of the Commissioners' by a later question, Webster said 'The working of the Commission virtually devolves on the clerk, as appears from the return made by him to the House of Commons, rather than to the Commissioners as a collective body'.[14]

The title 'Clerk of the Commissioners' had been added in 1852 to that of the 'Clerk of the Patents', a style so hallowed by long usage that it could only be dispensed with by Act of Parliament, a matter the 1852 Act did not deal with. In the opinion of the Commissioners it was better to allow the pre-1852 holder to retain the title and associated financial allowance rather than incur a heavy compensation outlay. There was, however, more involved than compensation costs. This particular 'Clerk' was also 'Reading Clerk in the House of Lords' and had friends in high places.

With establishment of the Patent Office 'the Clerk of the Patents' became head of its Patent Division with his pre-1852

'Deputy' in practical charge of that section. Woodcroft had been disappointed with his title of 'Superintendent of Specifications' but for ten years all seems to have gone comparatively smoothly, then problems arose leading to an Inquiry into Patent Office affairs. The Inquiry delved deep and unearthed material not in the 'Clerk of Patents' favour resulting in his resignation being requested. Following on from this Woodcroft was appointed 'Clerk to the Commissioners' and overall head of the Office.[15]

Woodcroft was in his early sixties by the time he held the title of 'Clerk to the Commissioners'. His memorial biographer could justly write (probably quoting fairly accurately his subject's personal observations), 'It was not his own fault that he did not accomplish much more, but during the earlier years of his official life his authority was not undivided, and he was thwarted by a system of concurrent jurisdiction which was introduced, most unwisely, by the Commissioners when the department was organised'. But did this 'unwise' decision of the Commissioners provide Woodcroft with an alibi? Prior to his official appointment Woodcroft had a history of enthusiastically starting projects. 'Woodcroft was a man of strong determination, and his mind once made up, he rarely swerved until his end was accomplished. When, however, success was attained, he not infrequently seemed disinclined to follow it up, and it was said of him that no sooner had he by infinite pains and trouble brought an invention to perfection, than "he turned it out of doors" for anyone to appropriate who would'.[16] Having set his scheme of indexes and abridgments under way with apparent initial success did Woodcroft switch his interest elsewhere, say to his 'Patent Museum'? Certain it is that, when the indexing and abridging systems he had started with so much enthusiasm began to display weakness and need for revision, nothing appears to have been done to prevent deterioration to a position where they were a constant source of frustration and dismay to those whose business it was to make use of them.

One important matter over which neither the Commissioners nor Woodcroft could exert total control lay in the manner of disposal of patent fees. When Charles Abel and a great many others harped on the theme of the vast accumulation of 'surplus fees' in the hands of the Commissioners they overlooked the fact that, but for disbursements in day to day running of the Office, fees were paid into the Consolidated Fund–and the Treasury had many calls to make on this Fund unrelated to patent matters.

In spite of many shortcomings and obstacles to further change, the patent system provided enough satisfaction through three decades for ever increasing use to be made of it. For those seeking improvements one disappointment followed another, but the cause of patent reform never lacked supporters. New men were to come along whose names are associated with changes that eventually came to pass. Thomas Webster died before those changes took effect and his faithfulness to the cause through a quarter of a century has not been adequately acknowledged. The same is true of his services to the Society. It was he who took the lead in actions that saved the Society in the early 1840s when termination or absorption into another association with accompanying loss of distinctive ethos were real possibilities. When ruthlessly brushed aside by Henry Cole in the 1850s he did not quit but quietly continued his interest in the Society through another twenty years. Both in the Society and in the patent reform movement Webster constantly, and with no small amount of trouble to himself, pursued objectives which he considered to be for the good of both. Though a little exaggerated for Webster, some memorial phrases devised in more dramatic times seem not altogether inappropriate for him. 'Whose singular praise it was, to have done ye best things in ye worst times, and hoped them in the most callamitous.'[47]

7

'Down the ringing grooves of change'

'Say not the struggle nought availeth ... as things have been things remain'. Those looking forward to patent reform most keenly may have found little comfort with Clough but his 'not by eastern windows only, when daylight comes, comes in the light' was remarkably apposite to the patent situation as it unfolded. Reforms in a far wider context than patents had been earnestly sought throughout Clough's lifetime but not until after his death (1861) were there positive signs that a new day was dawning.

Progress on long-overdue changes in many areas of public life awaited an administration possessed with the resolution to confront powerful elements wedded to old ways. At the end of 1868 a ministry took office prepared to do so knowing that a surge of public opinion was with it. It set in motion thorough overhauls of the military organisation, the judiciary and the civil service. An Order in Council of 1870 abolished patronage in the civil service and entry to its ranks was to be by open competitive examinations. The basic structure of the service was to be of two divisions, one to consist of people of high academic attainment to perform intellectual work and provide leadership, and the other to be staffed by people competent to perform more routine duties.[1]

Perhaps because the recently established Patent Office displayed no resistance to the new regulations it was one of the first departments to receive a Higher Division recruit. He (the civil service was entirely a male province) provided a good example of the type of person expected to fill senior posts. After education at Harrow and Cambridge, Henry Trueman Wood entered the Patent Office in 1870, where he appears to have been well received by Bennet Woodcroft. His stay there was short, however, – less than two years – but long enough for him to acquire a sound background knowledge of the patent system. Recommended by an acquaintance to the post of editor of the *Journal of the Society of Arts*, he became a member of the Society's staff in 1872 and was a salaried officer for thirty-five years. These were followed, after formal retirement, by many years of service to the Society as a Council member, Chairman (1919–20) and Vice-President.

A mere three years into his editorship, Wood read a paper 'On the Registration of Trade Marks'.[2] This was a subject that had been on the Society's agenda from 1853 and, as with the patent issue, the Society had provided a focal point, a forum for discussion and an intercommunication centre for a diversity of groups scattered throughout the country. By the time of Wood's contribution (November, 1875) the trade marks registration pot was coming to the boil and his paper was delivered before a knowledgeable audience well versed in the subject. The ensuing lively discussion was continued the week following. Within a few months Wood was to open a debate on 'The Patents of Inventions Bill, 1877',[3] by which time he had been appointed Assistant Secretary. Promotion to Secretary followed quickly in consequence of the sudden death of Peter Le Neve Foster.

Le Neve Foster had been the Society's Secretary for twenty-six years. A barrister with wide scientific interests, he was a close contemporary of Thomas Webster with whom he was associated in the 1840s reforms of the Society and later in matters affecting patents.[4] He served on the 1849–51 'Committee appointed to promote Legislative Recognition of the Rights of Inventors' and was involved in the provisional patent protection arrangements preceding the 1851 Exhibition. Among his many interests outside the Society was the British Association for the Advancement of Science to which he was deeply committed, regularly attending its meetings over twenty years and serving on its Council and on other committees. From its earliest years the Association had shown especial interest in patent reform both in general and in some of its specialist groups, none more so than the Mechanical Science Committee for which Le Neve Foster was secretary for thirteen years.[5] But it was not only through the Society and the British Association that he displayed interest in patent reform; one group with which he was connected termed itself 'The Patent Law Committee, 1875'. This body met in the Council Room of the Institution of Civil Engineers. Its distinguished membership included many inventors from a range of disciplines and appears to have done sterling work in analysing and in providing detailed observations on at least one of the Bills introduced during the 1870s. Le Neve Foster was well acquainted with many of the sixty-five or so people whose names appear on its printed membership list, approximately a quarter of whom were also Society of Arts members. Some of these had already made their mark at the Society, such as Henry Cole, Lyon Playfair and Thomas Webster, and others were to do so, such as Frederick Abel, President of the British Association's Chemistry Committee in 1877,[6] and Frederick Bramwell, President of its Mechanical Science Committee in 1872 during Le Neve Foster's secretaryship and again in 1884 when Trueman Wood had taken over as that Committee's secretary.*

The 1875 'Patent Law Committee's' Chairman (and presumed initiator) was William Siemens.[7] He too had been President of the British Association's Mechanical Science Committee in the Le Neve Foster period and was also overall President of the Association in 1882. His interest in the patent system may be assessed from there being more than one hundred patents bearing his name at the time of his appointment as Chairman of Council of the Society of Arts (also in 1882). His signature was on the Society's Memorials to the Commissioners of Patents in 1856 and 1858 and on other corresponding petitions of the period, such as those submitted by the British Association and the Institution of Civil Engineers, all of which had to do with improved facilities at the Patent Office. A member of an innovative Prussian family, William Siemens had settled in England in 1844 where he was able to attend to the exploitation of new products devised by family members, while developing personal business interests

* A complete list of members of this 1875 'Patent Law Committee' is provided in Appendix XIII.

and inventions. His elder brother built up an extensive electrical concern in Germany while another brother went to Russia attending to family and personal interests there, as William did in Britain.

To an inventive family with trans-border interests the individualistic laws and practices of different nations provided unwelcome complications. Such difficulties were not, of course unique to the Siemens fraternity. As the nineteenth century progressed and industrial developments were more and more quickly taken up outside the region of origin, it became increasingly important to seek patent protection in more than one country. It was an issue inventors had to face seriously, but for patent agents whose responsibility it was to advise clients on the best mode of action and then to follow up by filing applications abroad where a medley of totally different laws and procedures existed it must have been a high risk business. Some inventions brought before them were of potentially great value to their clients but of even greater worth to the countries of primary activity; the Siemens' regenerative furnace, for example, was highly profitable for its devisors but, on the other hand, the cost savings resulting from its use in the steel and glass industries were enormous, giving immediate advantage to the firms quick to make use of it and to the countries – principally Britain – of early major use.

Some form of reciprocity between nations had long exercised the minds of people with patent interests. One of the groups seeking patent reform in 1850, 'The Association of Patentees and Proprietors of Patents', had specified as one of its objects 'International arrangements for a mutual recognition of the rights of inventors' and in 1858 a Bill was introduced (without proceeding very far) 'To make Provisions to secure International Patent Right'. However widely and long-desired some form of international agreement may have been, so far as Britain was concerned improvements in the national patent system had to take priority. Not until the 1870s did an occasion arise that gave opportunity for open discussion of the issues involved by representatives of several nations.

Notice that preparations were under way for a 'Universal Exhibition' to be held at Vienna in 1873 created similar responses among inventors and proprietors of national patents as had preceded the London Exhibition of 1851. 'Months before the opening of the Vienna Exhibition, the alleged unsatisfactory state of Austrian Patent Laws was largely discussed and commented upon in the English, and more particularly the American newspapers, and many manufacturers in both countries objected to send any articles to the Vienna Exhibition on that account'. As in Great Britain prior to its 1851 exhibition, in Austria a law granting temporary protection of inventions was hurried through. However, the opportunity was seized of convening a conference to consider international patent rights: a London journal noticed, 'There has assembled at the Jury Pavilion in the Exhibition grounds, the International Congress, convened for the purpose of considering the question of patent protections'.[8]

At the opening proceedings of this international gathering William Siemens was elected Congress President. Among the national Vice-Presidents were Werner Siemens for Germany and Thomas Webster for Great Britain. The Vienna Congress was followed by a conference at The Hague in 1875 when the London patent agent William Lloyd Wise (active in the Society's patent debates) read a paper on the assimilation of patent laws and a committee of British lawyers, including Thomas Webster, was appointed to consider it.[9] Webster died before this committee met but his place was taken by his son Richard.[10]

An incident in the early stages of the Vienna Congress brought out that the voice of the anti-patent movement was still to be heard in 1873. No sooner had William Siemens completed his speech as President early in the proceedings than an Austrian member of the Congress Council, a Professor Neumann of Vienna, took the floor as spokesman for an anti-patent group. 'He and his friends,' he said, 'though small in number as yet, were of opinion that the principle of liberty, i.e., the principles of free trade, must also be applied to inventions and patents. The latter were incompatible with the progress of our time, with free trade; they were opposed to all principles of liberty ...'[11] Even in continental Europe the anti-patent movement was soon to be a spent force, but in Britain the tide was on the turn, even if it were not immediately obvious at the time.

Some reasons for the changes giving rise to a more favourable flow of opinion in Britain towards patents had origins with no direct parallels in continental Europe. Although set in a different context the following observations on issues that became apparent following the Great Exhibition of 1851 have a bearing also on the patent situation. The first is taken from Trueman Wood's history of the Society; the second from a more recent writer:

> 'On his return from a visit to the Paris Exhibition of 1867, where he had been acting as one of the jurors, Dr. Lyon Playfair addressed a letter to Lord Granville commenting on the industrial progress which had been made by other countries as compared with that of Great Britain ... This state of things he attributed mainly to the advance which had been made on the Continent in technical or industrial education. As far back as 1853 Dr. Playfair had published a work on industrial education on the Continent, and had prophesied that the result of the attention given to such education abroad, and its neglect in England, would lead to a much more rapid industrial advance on the Continent than in England.'

> 'The year of jubilee (1887) prompted T.H. Huxley to sound a serious note: "We are entering," he wrote to *The Times* on 21 March 1887, "indeed we have already entered, upon the most serious struggle for existence to which this country was ever committed. The latter years of the century promise to see us in an industrial war of far more serious import than the military wars of its opening years." He indicated the menace both from the east (Germany) and from the west (America), and urged the organisation of victory in this "grave situation". ... The notion of an industrial army caught the public imagination, and the response to Huxley's appeal showed how little the parties were divided on the question. Forty MPs met in the Society of Arts (founded in 1754 and home of many earlier efforts to promote industrial education) together with delegates from school boards, trade unions, chambers of commerce, and other interested parties, to form a National Association for the Promotion of Technical Education. Familiar names appear among its officers: Sir Bernhard Samuelson, A.J. Mundella and Huxley himself.'[12]

Recognition of the need for improvements in technical education consequent on changes in the international economic scene was matched in the patent conscious community. Huxley's 'industrial war' required every available weapon to be sharpened. In addition, trade depression in the 1870s and 80s brought home to all but the most insular that old methods, old machines, old concepts, however meritorious in their days, could lack competitive edge in a world that did not stand still. Innovation and invention were seen more widely than before as primary elements in economic change. Politicians got the message – and made use of it. 'The great salient feature of the age is in its first aspect the constant discovery of the secrets of nature, and the progressive subjugation of her forces to the purposes and will of men', declaimed Gladstone in 1879. A few months after delivering this opinion he was again Prime Minister, heading a government that (with a little help from the Society of Arts) was to see through a long-desired enactment affecting patents.

Looking back over a difficult period for patents during an address to the Society in 1883, Frederick Bramwell offered an analysis of the changing scene that also merits extensive quotation:

> 'It cannot be doubted, that in England, some ten years ago, those who held themselves out as the leaders of thought and of opinion were, as a rule, opposed to patents. The political economist and the freetrader detested them as conferring monopolies; the lawyer detested them because he might have either as counsel to argue upon them, or as judge to preside at a jury trial, or without a jury even to decide a patent action; and, whether as counsel or judge, he had no kindly feeling towards that which gave him extra trouble, by involving him in the consideration of matters which, except in rare instances, were foreign to his ordinary pursuits and train of thought. In fact, patent cases were a deal more troublesome than those for "goods sold and delivered," and they did not accord the amusement of a prolonged action relating to a racy libel, or other *cause célèbre*. The successful manufacturer disliked patents, because the development of the inventions covered by them might interfere with his established business, carried on in a way that he understood; might cause his existing plant to be superseded, and be reduced to the value of old metal; thus inflicting on him

> the double annoyance of having to go to school in his mature age to re-learn his business, and to find fresh capital to purchase new plant. The man engaged in pure science was no friend of patents, he was occupied with the discovery of principles and of laws. About eight or nine years ago, however, I am glad to say, the current of opinion ceased to flow so strongly against patents. Some of the political economist opponents, seeing the great progress of the manufacturing industries of America, and knowing of the prevalence of patents there, had it forced upon them that the existence of patents did not of necessity hamper trade. Many of the younger race of lawyers had included scientific subjects in their education, and were not averse from questions involving either mechanics, chemistry, or physics. Manufacturers, even with old established businesses, had recognised that if they would not come forward, others, either at home or abroad, would do so; and had thought that it was better to keep a leading position, at the cost of some trouble and some money, than to allow themselves to be passed by others. The literary man also found the difficulty growing upon him, the more he studied it, how to discriminate between copyright and patent-right, and to see why the description of a new invention should be protected by copyright if the invention itself was to be without any protection whatever. In fact – to use a figure borrowed from the behaviour of tidal rivers – we may, I think, at the present day, say that not only is the adverse downward current flowing with less strength, but there are, as there are at the turn of the tide in a river, currents making their way in the opposite direction.'[13]

The Society's *Journal* for 5 August, 1882 made public the essential elements of a Bill prepared by a committee of the Society comprising Frederick Abel, Frederick Bramwell (as Chairman), Alfred Carpmael, Henry Cole, Douglas Galton, William Perkin, William Siemens and Trueman Wood. (Abel, Bramwell, Cole, Galton and Siemens were all Chairmen of Council over a spread of years; Carpmael was from a family of patent agents and legal advisors with a very long connection with the Society; Perkin, a chemist, pioneered the development of synthetic dyes.[14]) The Bill put together by this committee provided the subject of a paper read by Bramwell before the Mechanical Science Section of the British Association with William Siemens in the chair. Bramwell's paper and some contributions to the ensuing discussion were published in full in the Society's *Journal* of 30 September, 1881. The British Association had its own committee on Patent Legislation (with Bramwell as secretary) which had already submitted to Parliament the Association's suggestions for patent reform. Notwithstanding that a report of the activities of this committee immediately preceded the reading of Bramwell's paper, Siemens told the meeting during the discussion following, 'The Patent-law worked out nominally by the Society of Arts, but in reality by my excellent friend, Sir Frederick Bramwell, is, I think, the best considered, and, perhaps, the most perfect attempt at a just and equitable law on the subject; and I, as one of the committee, can only hope that it will find favour in this Section in order that it may be strengthened by the weight of the British Association. ... You may depend upon it that all the questions [that had arisen in discussion] have been very carefully considered by the committee, and also tested by legal opinion.'

At the time of presenting the Society's Bill to its Mechanical Science Committee, Frederick Bramwell had been a regular attender at the British Association's meetings for some sixteen years and had already performed the duties of President of the Section he addressed. Among several other organisations in which he was active and held office were the Institutions of Civil (to which he was especially attached) and Mechanical Engineers; he served on the Councils and as President of both. Already leading a very full life when elected to the Society of Arts at the age of fifty-six it would hardly have been surprising if he had been content to take a passive role in its affairs, yet Trueman Wood wrote of him: 'His record of service to the Society is second to none. He read several papers, and delivered a course of Cantor Lectures. He constantly occupied the chair at its meetings and still more frequently took part in its discussions. He served in every capacity on its Council from 1875 to 1893, and the list of the offices he filled was completed by his election to the post of President in 1901, in the interval between the accession of King Edward VII, and the acceptance of the Presidency by the Prince of Wales (King George V).'[15]

Sir Frederick Bramwell, Bart

Trained as an engineer, Bramwell had early found a niche as consultant and expert witness, particularly in patent cases. (His elder brother attained eminence at the bar and on the bench.) By the time he joined the Society in 1874 his knowledge of patent law and practice was great and his facility for clear exposition of mechanical – and patent – matters was highly regarded. It was a remarkable turn of fate that brought him to the Society only a short time prior to the sudden and quite unexpected death of Thomas Webster. In the years immediately preceding the enactment of the first major piece of patent legislation since the Act of 1852, Bramwell's position was not dissimilar to that of Webster prior to that date.

Bramwell introduced himself to the Society at large a few weeks after his election by giving a lucid and telling lecture on 'The Expediency of Protection of Inventions'.[16] In this he dealt point by point with arguments raised in opposition to patents. During the discussion that followed, William Newmarch, FRS, Corresponding Member of the Institute of France, observed with some justification that 'after the paper they had just heard, it really required some amount of ingenuity to see what could be said on the other side.' This speaker also gave credit to Bramwell for turning opinion 'during the last four or five years' away from the 'very formidable manifestations in favour of abolishing protection'. The lively post-lecture discussion was continued the following week, a not unusual occurrence after papers relating to patents. (It had occurred following Trueman Wood's paper on the 1877 Bill when Bramwell was a contributor to the discussion. A meeting in May, 1879 for the reading of a paper by William Lloyd Wise on 'The Government Patent Bill' was chaired by Bramwell, and his British Association lecture and address to the Society as Chairman of Council followed in the autumn of 1880. Fifteen months later, on returning from a visit to the USA, where he had made a point of discussing American law and practice with a variety of people acquainted with patents, he read a further paper before the Society under the title 'The Society of Arts Patent Bill, and some Points in American Law and Practice bearing thereon'.[17]

This last paper he preceded with the information that 'it has been arranged with Sir John Lubbock that the Patent Bill prepared by the Society, last year, shall be re-introduced in the Session of Parliament now about to commence, and shall be re-introduced without alteration whatever'. This was the Bill William Siemens had recommended to the British Association as 'the most perfect attempt at a just and equitable law on the subject', nevertheless, it had gone the way of a succession of abortive Bills of the 1870s. Its proposed re-introduction was a non-starter, because the Government had prepared its own Bill which passed onto the Statute Book in 1883 within a few months of Bramwell's talk on US law and practice.

In the 'American Law and Practice' lecture, Bramwell was scornful of the 1852 system of Commissioners of Patents – 'a body of lawyers, all of whom, with one exception, vanish with the government of the day, to be succeeded by a fresh set, who, by the time they have learnt something of their business – assuming they had even leisure from their other duties to learn it at all – have in their turn to disappear'. Then he went on, 'By Clause 8 of the Society's Bill they propose that the management of the Patent-Office shall be under three Commissioners, one of whom shall be experienced in engineering, one in chemistry, and one in law'. It is fascinating that Bramwell, immediately returned from the USA, telling his audience how much better generally patent matters were approached there and expressing warm appreciation of the help he had received from the head of the US Patent Office, still had his mind set by 1852 concepts in at least one respect. Someone in the Government may have looked at US practice with more open eyes, for the Bill introduced by the President of the Board of Trade proposed that the UK Patent Office should be administered in a similar way to that of the US. It was to be taken out of the hands of Commissioners and placed under a single Comptroller responsible to the Board of Trade.

Bramwell was not alone in being committed to established practice in this regard. Richard Webster was appalled at what the Government (not of his party) proposed. He told a meeting of the Society, 'From some practical knowledge of the working of the present system, I should say that the abolition of the Commissioners of Patents as a body, and the substitution of one Comptroller, would be practically unworkable ... it was almost absurd to suppose that the work which the Society's Bill proposed to leave to a competent body of commissioners, could be properly performed by any single Comptroller.'[18] 'Almost absurd' and 'practically unworkable' though it seemed to men steeped in the practice of their time it passed into law and endured. This administrative change may appear in retrospect to have been a minor improvement on the prevailing system, but when it is remembered that the granting of invention patents had lain within the jurisdiction of the Lord Chancellor and the Law Officers (three of the four practising Commissioners of Patents of the 1852 Act) for more than three hundred years (and patents of other sorts for as long again), it may be appreciated how great a break with the past it signified. Medieval links had at last been broken and the patent system took a major step into the modern era.[19]

The Government's Bill, which passed into law to take effect from the first day of January 1884, contained a section requiring every patent application to be referred to an examiner. This also was a new feature but, unlike the creation of a Comptroller, was not unexpected. No aspect of patent practice had been ventilated as frequently over the previous twenty years; hardly surprising then that the debate on examination did not end with the entry into force of the 1883 Act. For those who did not persist in outright opposition the arguments were merely narrowed, principally to the merits or otherwise of requiring some form of investigation into the 'newness' of each alleged invention. Speaking in the House on the 1883 Bill Joseph Chamberlain, President of the Board of Trade, had made it clear that the Government was not against a novelty search in principle but baulked at the cost. It was, notwithstanding, the Government's intention that inventors should have every facility to enable them to carry out searches for themselves. Limited investigation for novelty by Patent Office examiners was included in an Act of 1902.[20]

The 1883 Act paved the way for ratification by the United Kingdom of the Paris Convention for the Protection of Industrial Property (also of 1883) in which more than 150 countries now have an interest. This was the first general international treaty in the field of patents and associated industrial or intellectual property, long desired but of the stuff that patent reformers' dreams were made of until the 1873 Patent Congress at Vienna began the process of converting dreams to reality. Successful adoption by founding states of the Paris Convention only ten years after the Vienna Congress owed much to the labours of William Siemens, Thomas Webster, William Lloyd Wise and many others. Some were active members of the Society of Arts and through them the Society may claim to have had a share in the creation of 'the International Convention'.

Apart from the polishing of jewels from time to time and the formulation of fresh procedures to keep abreast of ever-changing circumstances, the basic structures provided by the patents element of the Act of 1883 stood for almost a century. Patent laws and practices in other countries have been modelled on them.

From the 1780s when a committee of patent holders began to agitate for reform of the law[21] to the 1883 enactment had been a long haul. Individual Society of Arts' members had laboured in the cause throughout, but not until the late 1840s had the Society itself taken up the issue. By then many groups large and small, nationally based and local were pressing for action. It was the general esteem in which the Society was held in consequence of almost a century of encouraging innovation, and the influence its well-informed and well-regarded supporters could bring to bear, that allowed the Society to take the lead so that the Patent Law Amendment Act of 1852 has often been regarded as Society of Arts inspired. Throughout the 1850s and later the Society followed the application of the Act with an interest that took practical form in petitions and other kinds of representations commenting on the manner in which the Act was being put into effect.

Writing in his history of the Society, Trueman Wood said of the 1883 Act: 'A comparison of the Society's Bill [introduced in 1882 and again in 1883] with that which eventually passed into law will show to what a large extent the Act was founded on the Society's Bill'. Herbert Harding, who had studied the documentation of the period thoroughly, observed briefly, 'The Act of 1883 implemented practically all the recommendations of the Select Committee of 1872, except one, the ascertainment of the novelty of the invention'.[22]

What is clear is that for half a century from 1850 the Society provided a place where every shade of opinion regarding patents could be discussed and nowhere did the patent question receive such prolonged and thorough airing as in the Society's house.[23] Reports of official inquiries apart, there can surely be no comparable source of reference to nineteenth century attitudes and developments in this field than the Society's *Journal*. Substantially every major protagonist from 1852 onward would appear to have had his views recorded there.

In opening his Chairman's Address to the Society in 1882 William Siemens referred to his recent Presidential Address to the peripatetic British Association, which by that date had been giving serious consideration to patent matters including appointing committees each year, and then observed on an important distinction between the two bodies: 'There is an essential difference between the British Association and the Society of Arts, that the former can only take an annual survey of the programme of science, and must then confide to individuals, or to committees, specific enquiries to be reported upon ... at subsequent [annual] meetings; whereas the Society of Arts, with its 3,450 permanent members, its ninety-five associated societies, spread throughout the length and breadth of the country, its permanent building, its well-conducted *Journal*, its almost daily meetings and lectures, extending over six months of the year, possesses exceptionally favourable opportunities of following up questions of technical progress to the point of their practical accomplishment.'[24] Patents – *mutatis mutandis*.

8

Odds and Ends

Under the Act of 1883 the head of the Patent Office was to be known as the 'Comptroller' – or more fully, 'the Comptroller-General of Patents, Designs and Trade Marks'. The first bearer of this high-sounding title (and very likely its originator) was Henry Reader Lack, a member of the Society of Arts for a couple of decades and–in spite of few attendances at Council Meetings or other indications of zeal for the Society–a Treasurer for four or five years. He was a scion of an old Board of Trade family[1] and collateral kinsman of a Lack who had been a very senior clerk at the Board almost a century earlier i.e. at a period when the Society's Secretary was from time to time summoned to provide the Society's views on various matters.

Reader Lack had moved (temporarily as it transpired) from service under the Board to become Clerk to the Commissioners of Patents on the 'retirement' of Bennet Woodcroft in the spring of 1876. Woodcroft, though over seventy years of age at the time, did not take 'retirement' quietly and added to the problems awaiting Lack when he took office.[2] Great though the problems were when he became Clerk to the Commissioners, Lack added to this inheritance with aplomb and all the self-assurance and urbane composure of the well-connected. The anguish of Patent Office users was great and eventually came to the notice of the President of the Board of Trade, who appointed a committee.

The legal gentleman commissioned late in 1885 to chair the committee to 'Inquire into the Duties of the Patent Office' had been elevated to the Lord Chancellorship by the time the Inquiry was seriously under way and it was he, as Lord

Sir Henry Reader Lack
First Comptroller-General of Patents, Designs and Trade Marks

Herschell, who chaired a session on a Saturday in May 1886 when the Secretary of the Society of Arts, Henry Trueman Wood, appeared as a witness. Of the four other Inquiry members present that day at least two were Society members well-acquainted with the witness – Sir Bernhard Samuelson,

M.P. and Sir Richard Webster, M.P. The latter opened and was responsible for most of the questioning: 'You are the Secretary of the Society of Arts ... And you have had a great deal to do with patents?' 'Yes. As you know I had something to do in drafting the Bill put forward on behalf of the Society of Arts in 1882 and 1883,' and in response to a later question 'I was employed in the preparation of Abridgments from 1872 to 1884'. As 1872 was the year of Wood's entering employment at the Society of Arts he had been working as a contract abridger through most of his time at the Society. In a later answer it appeared that he was still involved in this work in 1885, though to a reduced extent. So, the Society's Secretary had had a foot in both camps for twelve years, or more. When answering another question Wood observed, 'I see a good many inventors and would-be patentees at the Society of Arts'.[3] A hundred years earlier the Society's then Secretary, Samuel More had been a witness at trials of Arkwright's patents (1785) and had remarked, 'No man in the United Kingdom is so often consulted upon patents as I am'. It would appear that for a century or more the Society's house at the Adelphi was a point of first enquiry for many people contemplating taking out patents – a sort of Would-be-patentees Advice Bureau.

From More to Wood, association of the Society's Secretaries with patents was substantially continuous. Following More's death in 1799 a much-favoured candidate among Society members for the succession was Edmund Cartwright, a pioneering innovator with, eventually, eleven patents to his name. Cartwright stood down in favour of Charles Taylor, industrial chemist, inventor and a patentee much consulted on patent matters. When interviewed as successor to Taylor, Arthur Aikin told the Society's committee that he was at that time occupied in drawing up patents. It is quite likely that he was the leading person to be consulted on chemical patents throughout his Secretaryship. Whishaw and Scott Russell who followed were both patentees. Solly was a technical innovator and he, like Neve Foster, displayed an interest in the state of patent law throughout his Secretaryship. Apart from about three years when patronage triumphed over sense (1839–42) every Secretary of the Society over a period of approximately 150 years displayed some form of favourable appreciation of patents.

Among the membership, too, appreciation of patents was general, even when officially the Society was having nothing to do with them. During those years there was an ever-increasing number of patentee-members, most of whose contributions to technical progress are now little known. There were, of course, names of many remembered and respected icons of the Industrial Revolution on the Society's Subscription Lists, such as Matthew Boulton, Josiah Wedgwood, Richard Arkwright and Robert Stephenson, but they were few in comparison to the many whose improvements now appear of little consequence being either directed to needs of their times now superseded and largely forgotten, or to secondary industrial features which may still have relevance to the amenities of modern life though in ways unseen and unregarded.

This last point has been mentioned earlier both in respect of subjects for which the Society offered awards and those appearing in lists of patented inventions, but it is a point so commonly overlooked as to merit further mention. Industrial development has its icons; 'Some there are that have left a name behind them to be commemorated in story', but 'There are others who are unremembered, they are dead and it is as though they never existed'.[4] Technological progress is not through icons alone.

Reverting more specifically to Society of Arts' activities, and again as mentioned earlier, the people who sat on the Society's practical arts committees often did so over prolonged periods as they examined the merits of subjects put forward for awards, often having to devise methods of testing or comparison. Members of the Committees of Agriculture, Chemistry, Manufactures and Mechanics were the work-horses without whom the Society could not have progressed and would not have endured. Unremembered, unrenowned, few have received mention in the chronicles of the Society.

As the Society moved forward from the mid-nineteenth century and away from being a purely premium-giving body into one whose main object became the dissemination of information about the industrial arts and sciences, and the publication of new discoveries and inventions of an industrial character, the need for the specialized practical arts committees declined. This decline coincided with a change independent of the Society but profoundly affecting it, this was the development of professional institutions. People who had been happy to serve on the Society's committees found – as the nineteenth century progressed – congenial association in specialized institutions. The Institution of Civil Engineers was well established by 1840; the Chemical Society held its first meeting in March, 1841 in the Society's house, electing as its first treasurer the recently retired Secretary of the Society soon to be its President; the Mechanical Engineers' body followed five years later; and so it was with other specialisms throughout the century.

One professional group affecting the Society did not coalesce until the century was fully three-quarters through. These were the patent agents. The century had begun with few patents being granted, the number of applications increased gradually before entering an entirely new phase of growth after 1852 leading to many more specialist advisors being required. Activity that had provided largely part-time work for comparatively few lawyers and practical men[5] suddenly became a full-time occupation for many, not all of them highly skilled. Even by the time of the 1864 Inquiry disquiet was being expressed concerning the quality of advice being provided. Inventors of limited means sometimes received poor – or useless – service from people advertising themselves as patent agents who had few, if any skills, other than ability to persuade impecunious inventors that protection of their ideas was safe in their hands. Although the object of the 1885 Committee of Inquiry was directed to matters at the Patent Office, opportunity was taken by the president of the largest group representing the interest of patent agents to urge that action be taken to ensure that agents were properly qualified. The outcome was an Act in 1888 disentitling any person from describing himself as a patent agent unless registered under rules to be prepared by the Board of Trade. The Board delegated the duty of maintaining the register and attending to matters relating to qualifying examinations to the Institute of Patent Agents, a body that had taken formal shape in 1882 and was to receive a royal charter in 1891. Not all patent agency problems had been solved by that year but by the end of the century the Chartered Institute was well in control of matters.[6]

Following the 1883 Patents Act, by which every application

had to be referred to an Examiner, debate in the Society rumbled on concerning the extent of the scrutiny to be made by those Examiners. An Act of 1902 introduced a limited investigation for novelty but this did not put an end to the debate. In December, 1904 Charles Denton Abel, some of whose observations at the time of the 1863/4 Royal Commission have been quoted, read a paper to the Society entitled 'The Patent Laws'.[7] This contribution to the long-running consideration at the Society's House of this controversial subject turned out to be a more noteworthy event than could be appreciated at the time. No single subject had taken up so much of the Society's time for over half a century, while patents had intruded upon the Society's business for nearly a century before. The 1904 meeting represented the end of an era in the Society's long history, from that date patents ceased to be an on-going concern.

There appeared no longer cause for the Society to meddle with so polemical a topic as patents. An established body of patent agents, a specialized patent bar, an active Inventors' Institute and a reformed Patent Office all provided their own opportunities for discussion, and when occasion arose for representation to that arm of government to which patent matters had been delegated – the Board of Trade. The pattern of the Society's interests had been altering in other ways as well. By the mid-1860s the original object of encouraging improvements in the practical arts by offering monetary awards or medals was drawing to a close; its exhibitions of industrial products and processes – at first national and then international – had ceased; also its encouragement of Mechanics' Institutes to raise standards of education among artisans followed by the establishment of a system of technical examinations had been rounded off by the transference of responsibility for those examinations to the City and Guilds Institute; and most of the many schemes involving the practical and industrial arts to which the Society had devoted time and resources had by the end of the nineteenth century been completed. By that time also, fundamental reform of the patent system had been achieved with the Society's help and in that area too the Society's work was done. From a low ebb around 1840 the Society had been revived to grow from strength to strength, its membership rising five-fold to the mid-1880s, though it declined as the century closed. An uncertain century opened with a shrinking membership list and without stimulating projects in hand comparable with the many successfully accomplished during the previous half-century. It survived; 'New occasions teach new duties; Time makes ancient good uncouth ...'

9

'And Finally – '
Partisan Thoughts on a Nineteenth Century Evangelical Revival

Reference has been made to the parlous condition of the Society of Arts in the 1830s. In 1842 it was close to extinction but from that year may be dated a revival as surprising in its swiftness as beneficial in its long-term consequences. Why that revival happened provides a more difficult problem than the simple factual one of who were the people to initiate it and carry it through. What were their motives? Why the sudden outburst of activity in 1842 when it had been clear for all with eyes to see that the Society was in a decline which bore all the signs of being terminal? One who had eyes to see was Arthur Aikin (Secretary 1817–39); according to Trueman Wood, Aikin 'realised that the time had come for a change in the Society's methods and he did his best to initiate such change'. But Wood had reason to believe that Aikin 'could never get his ideas properly supported by the influential members of the Society'.[1] On retiring from the Secretaryship, Aikin became a Life Member and immediately took over the Chair of the Committee of Chemistry. He remained deeply involved with the Society.

Aikin had been specifically invited in 1831 to the Inaugural Meeting of the British Association for the Advancement of Science as Secretary of the Society of Arts and would be well aware of David Brewster's desire and hope that the Association would take up the issue of patent reform. No doubt Aikin (patentee and one-time drafter of patent specifications) shared the disappointment of many – including some keen Society of Arts members – when the Association did not pursue the subject. With no serious headway made in patent reform during the 1830s and with the British Association on which hopes had been pinned unwilling during that decade to add patents to its agenda, many must have been looking around for an organisation of some standing that could focus opinions and promote proposals. The Society of Arts was such a body, but it would first have to cast off some out-dated rules that had been good and desirable in their day but were limiting in the changed circumstances of the nineteenth century.

The manner and nature of the appointment of Aikin's successor in 1839 and the condition of the Society's finances presented cogent reasons for taking further the changes begun by Aikin. No doubt it was the same 'influential people' who had thwarted Aikin's other concepts for change who brought about the rejection of the report of the 'Special Committee' appointed late in 1841 to consider the Society's circumstances and to make recommendations regarding them. Members of this committee seem to have formed a determined group for, in spite of the 'influential' opposition and a fifteen month hiatus, they brought back the same report and by a device that side-stepped the 'influential members' obtained its acceptance.

What Trueman Wood described as 'a very judicious report' had been prepared by the 'Special Committee' and placed before a General Meeting of the Society a mere four weeks from the Committee's appointment. It set out a series of 'causes which have contributed to the present state of the Society' including the rise of other societies dealing with 'useful knowledge and scientific pursuits' resulting in 'the diminished funds of this Society, whose great object is the promotion of the useful arts rather than the personal gratification of its members'. (A tilt at the British Association?[2]) Other suggestions and observations included, 'the principal object of the Wednesday evening meetings should be the reading and discussion of communications on the arts and manufactures of the country' and that 'the exclusion of patented inventions from awards had been extremely detrimental to the interests of the Society'.[3] Action was taken very speedily to rescind the Rule relating to patents and to include in the reading of papers references to patented inventions. (See Appendix VIII, the *Trans.* Vol.LV reference.)

Although the Society's future was gravely in doubt–the rejection of the 'Special Committee's' report early in 1842 and ill-effects consequential on opposing proposals creating mayhem for the remainder of that year and almost bringing the shutters down–Webster and a few associates[4] embarked on a recruitment drive. Webster introduced eight new members to the Society in that year (which appears to be the same number as the total elected throughout the whole of the previous decade); John Bethell introduced nine, including a Dr. Christopher Irving who then introduced two more before the year was out; Edward Solly and his son brought in six. Of additional interest was that Webster, Bethell and Solly were all recent members (Bethell 1836, Webster and Solly 1838. Peter Le Neve Foster who appears not to have been overtly associated with the recruitment drive but is, nevertheless, said to have been a Webster supporter entered in 1837.) Some of the recruits are worth noting also: Bethell brought in William Newton, a very early patent agent and his son, and the railway engineer Robert Stephenson; Webster brought in William Carpmael, engineer and early patent agent, and others believed to be patent agents; the Newtons and Carpmael soon introduced more patent agents, and other members of that profession followed.

In retrospect it would seem that the small salvation band was merely tuning up in 1842 for a major campaign to follow. Towards the end of that eventful year, the Secretary–but recently appointed in succession to Aikin–resigned and immediate action had to be taken to maintain the regular work of the office. Webster offered to seek out a suitable stop-gap replacement. By January, 1843 he had sounded out Francis Whishaw and gained his agreement to put his name forward. Whishaw, formally installed as temporary Secretary three months later, was an engineer with many inventions to his credit, with an extensive knowledge of many aspects of his profession and with a wide range of acquaintances. Whatever activity he took up he threw himself into wholeheartedly. In an obituary memoir (1856) he was credited with introducing 140 new members to the Society;[5] but as Secretary he was not in a position to propose members, so whatever truth lay in that statement would lie concealed under other names. What can be discovered is that in the three years 1843–5 221 members were elected (the total membership in 1840 did not exceed 800 to which 36 were added in 1842). Webster and Bethell are recorded as together proposing 75; Bethell's Dr. Irving proposed 15; Charles Holtzapfel, an engineer well-known to Whishaw, added 13; George Bailey and Edward Speer (shortly to be the first Joint Chairmen of Council) contributed 10 and 7 respectively; Arthur Aikin, Benjamin Rotch and William Tooke each chipped in with three.[6]

Although many professions were represented by the members elected as a result of the 1840s recruitment campaign, it was to be expected having regard to the personalities providing the initial driving force that engineers, inventors and patent practitioners should represent a disproportionately large part of the input. Several recruits had been or continued to be members of the waning Mechanical Sciences Section (Section G) of the British Association which was near extinction by 1845. Though irrelevant to the present argument mention of a cognate activity of the Association and the Society seems not entirely inappropriate here. The Association's Mechanical Sciences Section had been responsible from 1838 for organising exhibitions of manufactures in conjunction with the Association's annual meetings. It could hardly be coincidence that an early enterprise of the rejuvenated Society was a small exhibition of mechanical inventions. This undertaking in 1846 could have been deemed a failure had not persistence led to better events in later years, including the 1851 Exhibition.[7] Exhibitions were not entirely new to the Society; its Repository was a permanent display of objects useful in the practical arts and as early as 1761 it had put on a special exhibition of agricultural and other machines.

Beginning with the appointment of the 'Special Committee' late in 1839 revival came swiftly and effectively, opening the way to wider horizons and a broader field of usefulness for the Society. But why did it happen? That it happened is fact: how it happened can be seen from the records, but why? What was the life-sustaining message the apostles communicated to receptive hearers and which early converts transmitted to others? 'Now is the time for all good men and true to come to the aid of the Society'? Such a call may affect dormant members but is unlikely to stir people hitherto well aware of the Society's existence without displaying active interest in it. Yet, it seems, it was the time for a great many good men and true to join the Society, some of them bestowing on it of their time and treasure in abundance. With what object? Was it not that they were inspired by an old message dressed in new garments; the message that had gone out from a small band of enthusiasts meeting in a Covent Garden coffee house in 1754 that saw merit in a commitment to encouraging improvements in the practical arts, manufactures and commerce? Ninety years on from the objectives set out by the founding fathers the arts and manufactures were largely industrial but still open to improvements. The improvers–innovators and inventors–were still worthy of awards, whether of prizes or medals or such encouragement as an imperfect patent system could provide. This last was manifestly open to improvement.

Desire to improve the patent system **may** not have been the principal reason behind the revival of the Society but, both among the initial revivalists and among those who heeded their message, there was considerable patent interest. They included some who had been disappointed with the British Association's lack of interest in the subject during the 1830s and for whom an old, respected and revitalised Society gave hope. While those with patent interests were doubtless in the minority, they were an active, vigorous, hard-working and determined minority. For someone with feet fixed firmly in each camp it is a satisfying thought that members with patent interests were to the fore in ensuring the revival of the Society in a time of crisis and that within a decade the Society was a prominent force in the reformation of a patent system in desperate need of improvement.

Notes and References

Notes to Chapter 1

1. The Rev. James Booth, LLD, FRS, Chairman of Council, at the opening of the Society's 102nd Session, 23 November 1855; *S of A Jnl.*, Vol.4, (1855–6), p.1.
2. Members who were proprietors of patents included such well-known figures as Richard Arkwright, Matthew Boulton and Joseph Bramah. Bryan Donkin, a Vice-President of the Society held many patents; his co-chairman of the Committee of Mechanics, Thomas Gill, was a patentee engaged in activities such as are now performed by patent agents. Of the Society's Secretaries, Samuel More (Secy. 1769–1799) claimed 'No man in the United Kingdom is so often consulted upon patents as I am who gets nothing by it'. More was followed by Charles Taylor (Secy. 1800–1816) a patentee and authority on patent practice. Taylor's successor, Arthur Aikin (Secy. 1817–1839) who was also a patentee, told the Society when he was interviewed for the post that he was occupied in drawing up patents. (See James Harrison; 'Some Patent Practitioners associated with the Society of Arts', *RSA Jnl.*, Vol.130 (1982), pp.494–497, 589–594, 670–674; annexed hereto.)
3. D.G.C. Allan; *William Shipley – Founder of the Royal Society of Arts* (1968).
4. Derek Hudson and Kenneth W. Luckhurst; *The Royal Society of Arts 1754–1954*, (1954), pp.8 and 9, including 'It being the Opinion of all present that ye Art of Drawing is absolutely Necessary in many Employments Trades and Manufactures, and that the Encouragement thereof may prove of great Utility to the public, it was resolved to bestow Premiums on a certain Number of Boys and Girls under the Age of Sixteen, who shall produce the best pieces of Drawing'.
5. From the early days of the reign of Elizabeth I great efforts were

made to maintain and improve native supplies of gunpowder. Patents for saltpetre granted during those early days were continued in spite of bitter protests, for this material had to be obtained as a national necessity. '[The saltpetre patent] digs into every man's House, it annoys the Inhabitants and generally troubleth the Subject; for this I must beseech you to be contented. . . . For I must tell you the Kingdom is not so well furnished with Powder now as it should be' (the younger Cecil to the Commons). A Statute of 1624 directed against monopolies exempted saltpetre patents from its general terms. The saltpetre monopoly was set aside in 1641 but the Parliamentarians revived the practice of allowing patentees to dig for this essential commodity. (Abstracted from W. Cunningham, *The Growth of English Industry and Commerce* (1903), pp.60/61.)

6 Patent No. 697 dated 10 Feby. 1755, *Making saltpetre from vegetables,* was taken out in the name of Paul Nightingale of the City of London, Gent. The patentee does not appear to have been a member of the Society but a committee appointed to judge on the madder premium and comprising both members and non-members included a Mr. Nightingale of Cheapside (*Society of Arts' Minutes* (hereafter cited as *Soc.Min.*), Vol.1, pp.77 & 80; 7 & 14 Jany, 1756). In 1760 a Miles Nightingale of Cheapside and John Nightingale of Lombard Street were elected to membership.

7 Patent No. 749, *Making Isinglass from British Materials,* is dated 26 March 1760. The patentee, Humphrey Jackson, chemist of East Smithfield, was elected to membership of the Society in May, 1760 and paid annual subscriptions for three succeeding years. A committee to consider Mr. Jackson's patent and specification for making isinglass was appointed on 1 July, 1761. (*Soc. Min.*, Vol.VII, p.1). D.G.C. Allan, the Society's Historical Adviser, traced many succeeding instances of patents being granted in respect of subjects for which the patentees had earlier received awards from the Society. (See Appendix VI)

8 *Soc. Min.,* Vol.III, p.103, 15 Nov. 1758; letter from Mr. Joseph Oxley of Newcastle, 'he also mentions that he has constructed a Boulting Mill which greatly exceeds any yet made, but is not willing to make it public unless he has a Patent'; it was ordered that a letter be sent to acquaint Mr. Oxley the Society did not encourage the obtaining of patents, as in the main text.

9 Allan; *William Shipley, op.cit.*, pp.56 and 192. On the 5th February, 1755 when the Society's *Plan* was agreed and its first officers elected, Baker and Shipley were elected 'perpetual members'. (Hales was Vice President.) Although Shipley was appointed Secretary, Baker 'all along took the minutes'. H.T. Wood; *A*

History of the Royal Society of Arts (1913), pp.12 & 17. The phrase 'the employing of the poor' used in Baker's 'Plan' was more than a virtuous nod in the direction of philanthropy. It had its roots in 'the traditional notions of economic policy inherited by the Society ... from the "Mercantilist" writers of the seventeenth century. There was also the suggestion of a Christian concern to protect the poor from exploitation by the rich ...' D.G.C. Allan; 'Notions of Economic Policy expressed by the Society's Correspondents and in its Publications', *RSA Jnl.*, Vol.106 (1956), pp.800–804; Vol.107 (1959), pp.55–59 and 217–220 at p.58.

10 Allan and R.E. Schofield; *Stephen Hales, Scientist and Philanthropist* (1980).

11 A.E. Clark-Kennedy; *Stephen Hales, D.D., F.R.S.* (1929) p.244, *per* D.G.C. Allan in 'Dr. Hales and the Society, 1753–61', *RSA Jnl.*, Vol.111, (Dec.1963), pp.53–57 at p.57. Baker expressed similar sentiments to those of Hales when he felt moved to write of his contribution to the Society: 'All this I have done in private ... nor ever expecting the least advantage from my trouble ... The internal Satisfaction of doing Good has been to me a sufficient Reward.' (Society of Arts' Guard Books, Vol.XII, 120.) One of the Society's award seekers, of more humble circumstance than Baker, Hales or Shipley, had the same feelings about his novel agricultural implement as did Hales of his ventilators: 'Whether I shall get any Thing for my Trouble ... I know not ... but this I know, that I shall enjoy the hart-felt Satisfaction of contributing to the Prosperity of my Country in general, and that of every honest industrious Man in particular ... to see Old England once more a Land of Plenty will make me the happiest Man in it though I get but Bread and Cheese, and wear a thread-bare Coat as long as I live'. (Soc. Guard Books, Vol.X, 37.) Both the above letters are quoted in 'The Society's Early Days: New Light from its Correspondence' by a former Secretary of the Society, Kenneth W. Luckhurst; *RSA Jnl.*, Vol.102 (1952–4), pp.292–313.

12 J.S.P. Buckland, 'Savery's Steam Engine Workshop 1702', *Newcomen Society Transactions*, Vol.56, 1984/5, pp.1–20, more particularly pp.1 and 2. Denis Papin FRS worked on steam pumps and engines contemporaneously with Thomas Savery (1650?–1715). Papin favoured immediate disclosure of inventions, see Alan Smith, 'The 350th Anniversary of Denis Papin (1647?–1713)', *Newcomen Bulletin* No. 168, August 1997, pp.13–16, more particularly at p.14.

13 Peter Mathias, *The Transformation of England* (1979), pp.295–317; see more particularly 'he [Samuel Johnson] approved of making money through inventions and discoveries' (p.305) and his

support of the patentee Lewis Paul (pp.307–309).

14 Soc. Guard Books, Vols.XI (end) & IV, 104, *per* Luckhurst, *op.cit.*

15 *Soc. Min.*, Vol.VI, p.33; 1/10/1760.

16 *Soc. Min.*, Vol.1, p.48; 2/7/1755.

Notes to Chapter 2

1 Society of Arts' Manuscript Transactions (hereafter *Soc. Trans.*) 1774–5, pp.93 and 94. Also. *Soc. Min.*, Vol.XX. p.49, 4/1/1775: 'A Petition of Mr. Peter Debaufre with a printed Copy of his Patent for making Chips for Hats was Referred to the Committee of Mechanics. Ordered that he be summoned to Attend the Committee with his Tool and some of his Chips'. A letter from Peter Debaufre's journeyman, Robert Galloway, had been put to the Society on 23rd November, 1774 and referred to a committee. A communication from his employer read at the same meeting resulted in a resolution 'that Mr. Debaufre be informed that as he has obtained a Patent for his Invention the Society cannot consider it'. Chip hats had been introduced to the Society's premium lists in 1763, six years prior to Peter Debaufre's patent grant (No. 922 dated 21/3/1769 and entitled, 'Tools for shaving, cutting, and preparing wood for making Leghorn hats and bonnets'.) Had the Society's premium offer been Debaufre's original stimulus? On 18th January, 1775 'a Bounty of Twenty five Guineas was voted to Mr. Galloway for his Improvement of the Tools for cutting Chips for Hats'. Whether the Society acted correctly in making this award is debatable.

2 In considering patent costs of £210 and £125 comparison may be made for relative value purposes with the annual salary of £150 set for the Secretary of the Society of Arts who was expected to be 'a professional man'. However, he also had rent-free accommodation in a house adjoining the Society's building. (As a matter of interest a committee reported to the Society in 1760 regarding the Secretary to be appointed, 'that the proper conduct of the Society's work required a man of general and technical knowledge, able to deal with scientific questions and conversant with foreign languages' ... 'He ought to be a man of character and a man of learning' and such a man, the committee thought, 'might well deserve a salary of £200 a year'. The Society at large thought otherwise and settled for £150.) Wood, *op.cit.*, p.23.

3 A.A. Gomme, 'Patent Practice in the 18th Century: The Diary of Samuel Taylor, Threadmaker and Inventor, 1722–1723, *Newcomen*

Society Trans; Vol.XV, 1934–35, pp.209–224. Samuel Taylor expended an appreciable sum of money in small amounts 'encouraging' a variety of people to perform their duties without undue delay. The porter discharged by the Society in November, 1765 for accepting a gratuity of £5 from a candidate for a premium seems to have expected rather more for his services than was normal among corresponding functionaries in offices of state (see Wood, *op.cit.*, p.341).

4 William Martin, *The English Patent System* (1904), p.19.

5 *Soc. Min.*, Vol.I, p.126; 14/4/1756.

6 See, for example, Wadsworth and Mann, *The Cotton Trade and Industrial Lancashire 1600–1780 (1931)*, at pp.450–456 for John Kay's patent troubles, and pp.495–6 for Richard Arkwright's. L.T.C. Rolt, *James Watt* (1962), deals briefly with Boulton and Watt's infringement problems at pp.120–129; 'The weight of the attacks against the patent were now so great that notwithstanding any private misgivings the partners decided that they could no longer afford to bark at the opposition but must begin to bite'.

7 John Carey, *An Essay on the State of England* (1965) quoted in *Industry and Technology* by W.H. Chaloner and A.E. Musson (1965) at page 33 where they observe that 'the seventeenth century closed amid a remarkable burst of inventive ingenuity. In the decade 1660–9 only 31 patents were granted, but in the 1690s no less that 102 received the seal of royal approbation, a figure that was not surpassed until the 1760s.' (A consequence of the Royal Society's early activities? Among eight committees appointed in 1664 was 'Mechanical. To consider and improve all Mechanical Inventions'.) The following is extracted from the John Carey quotation:

> 'Silk stockings are woven: tobacco is cut by engines ... deal boards are sawn with mills; lead is smelted by wind furnaces ... Beside which, there is a cunning crept into our trades. The Clock-maker hath improved his art to such a degree that labour and materials are the least part the buyer pays for. The variety of our woollen manufactures is so pretty ... The same art is crept into navigation ... Cranes and blocks help to draw up more ... mines and pits are drained by engines and aqueducts ... '.

8 James Harrison, '"The Ingenious Mr. Yeoman" and some Associates', *RSA Jnl.*, Vol.145 (1997), more particularly at pp.53–59.

9 Allan, *William Shipley, op.cit.*, pp.42–44.

10 Hudson and Luckhurst, *op.cit.*, pp.74–75.

11 Figures are taken from a list supplied to an 1829 Inquiry by a Select Committee of the House of Commons; they appear as

Appendix B1 on p.216 of the *Committee's Report.*

12 *The Patent* 'by the Author of *The Graces*', 1776. This poem appears to have provided the inspiration and much of the factual material for a song sung at Covent Garden on 20th April 1798 by a celebrated comedian of the time and entitled 'Patents all the Rage'. This remarkable contribution to patent literature is set out in full in Appendix III.

13 Many examples of the Society's investigations into the merits of proposals for which awards were sought are to be found in Wood's *History, op.cit.,* more particularly at pp.147–309. Page 263 refers to an episode also divertingly recorded elsewhere by an unsuccessful applicant. The Premium offer at issue was 'for the greatest Improvement in the Stocking Frame'. According to Wood the large number of frames entered was set up in the 'machine room' and several expert workmen were employed to test them. In a letter to his wife in Derby dated 15th February 1765 Jedediah Strutt vented his chagrin at not being the successful applicant: 'Since my last the frames have all been strictly examined by six chosen stocking makers, several Frame smiths and some other judicious persons and last night the Committee met to receive their report which was ... that mine was the prettiest and best among them notwithstanding which after waiting till ll o'clock thro' the influence of two or three partial prejudiced persons we were told that none but the Sutton frame could be admitted'. (From R.S. Fitton and A.P. Wadsworth, *The Strutts and the Arkwrights*, 1958, pp.39/40.) There is obviously more to this story, but what is of immediate significance is that the Society brought together as assessors a group of people knowledgeable in the trade 'six stocking makers, several Frame smiths and some other judicious persons'. A not less interesting and really quite remarkable account of the early Society's attention to assessment in its award schemes is provided in Basil Harley, 'The Society of Arts' Model Ship Trials 1758–63; a study in the pre-history of ship model hydrodynamics', *RSA Jnl.,* Vol..142 (1994), pp.50–52.

14 Minutes of Evidence before *Select Committee of the House of Lords on the Designs Act Extension Bill*, p.8; evidence of William Carpmael, Engineer and Patent Agent, 12th March, 1851.

15 Letter to Mr. Phineas Cook of Sheffield, *Soc of A Letter Book 1770–1816*, p.43, March 1771. The operative section of this letter sets out the Society's terms for a reward so clearly and succinctly as to merit quotation (the letter is over Samuel More's signature): 'If [you] continue to think of taking out a Patent for the Invention of Your Auger this Society can proceed no further with it, as it is one of our Laws never to meddle with any Thing for which Patents are

granted. But if you should think it worthwhile to accept of a moderate Reward from this Society You may lay open Your Invention for the Benefit of the Publick and after a proper Tryal the Society will bestow on You such Bounty as they shall think it deserving. The Instrument shall not be seen by any person till I hear from You. I request the favour of You therefore to return me an answer as soon as Possible.' A post-script to the letter read, 'It will not be amiss for You to inform me what Bounty You may expect from the Society'. (Mr. Cook received thirty guineas.)

[16] Allan, 'The Society of Arts and the Committee of the Privy Council for Trade, 1786–1815', *RSA Jnl.*, Vol.109, (1961), pp.389–394, 629–632, 807–810, 979–980, more particularly at p.631.

[17] The Preface to the 1802 volume of the Society's *Transactions* was no doubt the work of Dr. Charles Taylor, then Secretary to the Society, and was prepared not very long after Ellenborough L.C.J. had pronounced Charles Tennant's grant of 1798 for a method of preparing materials useful in bleaching textiles a 'scandalous patent'. Taylor was a witness against Tennant in this action. Four years earlier he had been one of a group representing Manchester cotton and linen interests successful in opposing an application for a monopoly relating to bleaching by Anthony Bourboulon and another. Earlier at the request of 'Gentlemen of the County of York' he had opposed a patent petition relating to the printing of wool cloth using wood rollers. Grant was refused on the basis of disclosures in a patent of 1772 taken out in the names of four Manchester men, a shuttle-maker, a turner, a merchant and Charles Taylor, also described as a merchant. (Trade directories of slightly later dates refer to Taylor as 'cotton manufacturer, dyer and printer'.) Credit for the invention of roller printing of textiles is generally given to Thomas Bell whose engraved copper cylinders (patent no. 1378 of 1783) were an improvement on wood rollers. Taylor would also be well acquainted with the proceedings leading to the revocation of a patent acquired by Matthew Boulton for an oil lamp designed to reduce smoke and smell (no. 1425 of 1784, Ami Argand) for he was associated with the Boulton and Watt partnership through the apprenticeship of James Watt Jnr. to him and in other ways. In addition, the most decisive evidence in the demise of the Argand patent is said to have been that of T.H. Magellan, FRS, well known to Taylor who was present at some of his chemical experiments. However, the cancellation of Richard Arkwright's patent in 1785 was probably the most noticed in its day and the most recorded historically. The attack on this patent on behalf of Lancashire cotton men was almost certainly organised by Charles Taylor. Other noteworthy patents also came

to grief in the twenty or so years prior to 1802. The Courts were right to strike most of them down, though Arkwright, Tennant and others were able to build up very profitable enterprises on the basis of patents whose terms were curtailed. Such people would not have regarded their efforts to acquire and defend their grants as futile exercises. Taylor's death was noticed in the *Transactions* with the statement 'the opulence which flowed so exuberantly to many of his fellow-townsmen did not find its way to him'; it would not be surprising if the iron had entered his soul by the time he went to the Society for he was without doubt an outstanding industrial chemist to whom the textile industry was greatly indebted. (Information on textile bleaching and printing patents has been obtained in the main from Musson and Robinson's *Science and Technology in the Industrial Revolution*, Chap.VIII, pp.251–337, 'The Introduction of Chlorine Bleaching'.)

Notes to Chapter 3

1 A.A. Gomme, *Patents of Invention* (1946); M. Frumkin, 'The Early History of Patents for Inventions' (1947), *Trans. Newcomen Society*, Vol.XXVI, pp.47–56 (and also *Trans. Chartered Institute of Patent Agents*); W. Cunningham, *op.cit.*; and others. Frumkin sets out fully a Venetian ordinance of 1474 and cites earlier monopoly grants from 1332. Cunningham recites a preamble to a patent of Elizabeth I which may be illustrative of others – 'We therefore, greatly likying of all good services and wyse and learned inventions tending to the benefit of the commonwealth ... and myndinge ... to farther and advance the skilfull first fynder thereof graciously to reward ... as of a service done greatly to our honour and the benefit of our realm'. (The form of wording employed on most eighteenth century grants included the phrase 'We, being willing to give encouragement to all arts and inventions which may be for the public use and benefit ...') Gomme lists in some detail the steps through which a patent petition passed from its initial presentation to the application of the Great Seal.

2 E. Wyndham Hulme, Privy Council Patent Law, *Law Quarterly Review*, April 1917, pp.191–2. Hulme indicates that Dollond's case set a precedent when, after reference from the Privy Council to the Law Officers, the latter advised action in the Common Law Courts. Two points raised in Court were later accepted as good law; secret prior working by another party does not invalidate a patent, and a patent may be obtained for a method of performing

an operation as distinct from the mechanical means for effecting it.

3 The financial difficulties of the Adam Bros. arising from their involvement with the Liardet patent (and also an adventure into saltpetre manufacture) are mentioned in some detail in 'After the Adelphi ...' by Alistair J. Rowan, *RSA Jnl.*, Vol.122 (1974), pp.659–678, more particularly at p.668; for the far greater financial problems arising from the Adelphi project see Allan, *The Adelphi – Past and Present*, pp 41/42.

4 Martin, *op.cit.*, p.19: 'Passing on to the year 1778, we learn that the case of *Liardet v. Johnson* decided that the specification had by this time superseded the former "consideration" or reason for the grant, *viz.* the establishment of an industry and the instruction of others in the art. Henceforth, the main tests of validity of the grant were to be applied to the specification ... When this stage was reached, modern patent law, the bulk of which is centred in the specification, was already outlined.'

5 Eric Robinson, 'James Watt and the Law of Patents'; *Technology and Culture,* Vol.XVII, 1976, pp.115–139 more particularly p.125 *et seq.* Eric Robinson and A.E. Musson, *James Watt and the Steam Revolution* (1969), pp.213–228. Report of 1829 Select Committee – see Note 8 below, p.45; Evidence of Arthur Aikin: 'I should be inclined to allow Mr. Watt to have a monopoly of it [the principle of collecting steam in a separate vessel], provided in his specification he had given (**which he has not given**) all the details of the machinery employed by him at the time of taking out his patent.' Similarly at p.32: Evidence of John Farey: 'According to the ordinary practices of the Courts of Law in other cases, Mr. Watt's patent ought to have been annulled, for the insufficiency of the specification. ... If the merit of Mr. Watt's engine had not been so universally allowed at the time of those trials as to have obtained a leaning in his favour, his right could not have been established as a mere question of law.'

6 Fitton and Wadsworth, *op.cit.,* p.87.

7 Robinson, and Robinson and Musson, *op.cit.*

8 *Report from the Select Committee on the Law relative to Patents for Inventions.* Ordered, by The House of Commons, to be Printed, 12 June 1829.

9 W.O. Henderson, *Industrial Britain under the Regency 1814–18* (1968), p.164.

10 Harrison, 'Some Patent Practitioners etc.' *RSA Jnl.*, Vol.130, *op.cit.*, see more particularly pp.496 and 672.

11 *Report of the Select Committee of the House of Lords ... touching Letters Patent ...* (1851).

12 E.J. Hughes, *Hughes on Patent Laws: The Patent Laws of all Nations* (1854), p.11.

[13] Wadsworth and Mann, *op.cit.*, pp.495/6. 'It is important to remember how intense was the Lancashire feeling against protective patents – however much protection might be deserved – and to what extent manufacturers would go to defeat them. The powerful Manchester Committee for the Protection of Trade expressly directed itself against the grant of any patents, and in reporting on its achievements explained how "Caveats have been entered at the Patent Office against the obtention of any Patents that are likely to affect the trade or manufactures of this country, by which means the Committee has had and always will have early notice of every application for patents of that sort, and will thereby have an opportunity of opposing them and of bestowing, or at least recommending, some other mode of reward for ingenuity so as to prevent the pernicious effects of patents" (*Manchester Mercury*, Dec. 31, 1782)'. (It is not to the credit of these Lancashire manufacturers that in the most noteworthy case of their offering to bestow a monetary award, i.e. in the matter of Samuel Crompton's spinning 'mule', several reneged on their promises.)

[14] H.I. Dutton, *The Patent System and Inventive Activity during the Industrial Revolution, 1750–1852* (1984), p.42.

[15] At least seven Bills were brought before the House of Commons in seven years of the 1830s – one in 1832, two in 1833, one each in 1835, 1836, 1838 and 1839. One, reflecting the Society of Arts' full title, was 'for the better encouragement of the arts and manufactures'.

[16] Dutton, *op.cit.*, pp.42–51.

[17] Wood, *op.cit.*, p.345.

[18] Wood, *ibid.*, p.344.

[19] Allan, *RSA Jnl.*, Vol.112 (1963–4), p.877 (Book Review).

[20] Richard D. Altick, London's Royal Polytechnic Institution, *New Scientist*, 6 July 1978, pp.36/37. (Excerpt from The Shows of London – *A Panoramic History of Exhibitions, 1600–1862* (1978)).

[21] Wood, *op.cit.*, pp.336/7; 343; 336.

[22] *The Mechanics' Magazine*, Vol.XXXII (1840), pp.157 and 206/207.

[23] Wood, *op.cit.*, pp.346–8.

Notes to Chapter 4

[1] Henderson, *op.cit.*, pp.165/6.

[2] Many examples could be cited of the painstaking attention and extensive amounts of time devoted to consideration of subjects presented for awards by those prepared to perform these tasks.

The following are by no means atypical: In 1761 when dealing with but one of several proposals put forward for refining, or at least diminishing, the noxious smell of whale oil 'altogether thirty five meetings were devoted to this nauseating business' (Hudson & Luckhurst, *op.cit.*, p.123). During the same year, consideration of means for harnessing tides to provide power generated 'a plaintive note in one of the Minutes that "the committee have sat to June 25th inclusive 24 times on tide mills", and still their task was not complete' (*ibid.*, p.112). Deliberation and tests on a 'Swiss Engine for tearing up Trees' took up not less than fifteen months in 1763/4, while model ship trials extended over 1758–63 (see Note 13 of Chapter 2).

3 G.E. Mercer; 'Mr. More of the Adelphi', *RSA Jnl.*, Vol.127 (1979), pp.241/242.

4 With one possible exception, all the small early membership of the Society of Civil Engineers met at various times during the 1770s at the Society of Arts' Committee of Mechanics – on at least one occasion comprising the total membership of a meeting. The subjects discussed at these gatherings were often of great interest to them – tide mills, surveying instruments, augers, 'engines for tearing up trees' and the like. It must have been extremely useful to be provided with a venue and purpose for meeting and discussing practical matters with other members of the same nascent profession. The Society of Civil Engineers was essentially a social group of like-minded men; the Society of Arts committee was a place for discussion of practical matters. (For the early history of the Civil Engineers' Society, see Garth Watson; *The Smeatonians – The Society of Civil Engineers* (1989); the origin of the Institution of Civil Engineers is mentioned on p.43.)

5 *The Technical Repository*, Vol.1 (1822).

6 *S of A Trans.*, Vol.LV, (1845), preface p.xii.

7 Harrison, 'Some Patent Practitioners etc.', *RSA Jnl., op.cit.*, Vol.130, p.589.

8 Wood, *op.cit.*, pp.345/6. *Soc. Min.*, 1841/42; 3rd Nov., 18th Nov. *et.seq*. (See also Appendix IX.)

9 An immediate consequence of the Webster committee's suggestions was the resignation of the Secretary, Graham. It became necessary, therefore, to appoint a replacement quickly and Webster, lately Secretary to the Institution of Civil Engineers, agreed to find someone. Francis Whishaw, a member of the 'Civils' whose abilities would be well known to Webster, was appointed in a temporary capacity in April, 1843. (Wood, *ibid.*, p.348). According to the author of Whishaw's obituary *Memoir* for the 'Civils' 'perhaps the greatest of Mr. Whishaw's public services was

the direction of his energies to the resuscitation of the Society of Arts, which would probably have died a natural death, had he not opportunely assembled a few influential men who afforded him their support as Secretary . . . He was very energetic and successful in personally canvassing for members, inducing one hundred and forty new members to join within a few months'. (*Proc. Inst. Civil Engs.*, Vol.XVI, p.143.) If Wishaw did, indeed, have a hand in introducing 140 new members, it is to be expected that a very high proportion of them would be engineers or like-minded people with a favourable leaning towards patents.

10 Wood, *ibid.*, p.352.

11 *S of A Trans.*, Vol.LIV, (1843), p.155.

12 Examples of industrial espionage are numerous, one involving well-known names is provided by L.T.C. Rolt in *Great Engineers* (1962) at pp.76–81: The success of Matthew Murray's Leeds foundry and the superior quality of its workmanship caused Messrs. Boulton & Watt of Birmingham (then under the control of James Watt Junior and Matthew Robinson Boulton) great concern. 'The steps they took to discredit Murray, to steal his trade secrets and damage his interests are fully documented in the correspondence of the Birmingham firm and make one of the most remarkable stories of commercial brigandage on record.'

13 A changed view of patents by the judiciary was noticeable during the first half of the nineteenth century in contrast to the attitude of the administrators of the system still bound up in the rituals of earlier centuries. In evidence before the 1829 Select Committee Francis Abbott said, 'Generally speaking, I should say that the courts are not very liberal to patentees' (p.63), later remarking that even then some amelioration was under way – 'In some points of minor description, patentees are now dealt with more liberally than they were some 20–30 years ago; in Lord Kenyon's time every little thing would set aside a patent' (p.64). Fifteen years later Baron Alderson, hearing the case of *Russell v. Ledsom and ors.* observed that 'the Court was very anxious, as all Courts ought to be, if they can by any reasonable and fair means, to support valuable and useful inventions, and not to turn them aside lightly by any matter which is not the essence of the thing. In modern times the courts have been more liberal than they were in ancient times . . .' (*Carpmael's Reports of Patent Cases*, Vol.1, p.569 more particularly at p.586.)

14 Dutton, *op.cit.*, pp.57/58.

15 Hughes, *op.cit.*, pp.12/13.

16 The great services John Scott Russell performed for the Society and in the early preparatory work for the 1851 exhibition were

overshadowed by the later activities of Henry Cole. Before becoming Secretary to the Society, Russell was member of the initial 1845 committee organising the first national exhibition of the products of industry proposed by Francis Whishaw. This committee included Thomas Webster and Bennet Woodcroft (Wood, *op.cit.*, p.404). An RSA pamphlet, *The Great Exhibition of 1851: Some Extracts from the Records of the Royal Society of Arts* (1951), also sets out Russell's cardinal position in discussions preliminary to the Great Exhibition. See also: George Mahon, 'John Scott Russell and Henry Cole: Aspects of a personal rivalry at the Society of Arts', *RSA Jnl.*, Vol.115 (1969), pp.204–208 and 299–302.

17 *First Report on the Principles of Jurisprudence which Regulate the Recognition of the Rights of Inventors* (1850). (Report of the Committee appointed to promote Legislative Recognition of the Rights of Inventors.)

18 *Ibid.*, para.30. In the absence of reforming legislation prior to the 1851 Exhibition inventors were allowed temporary protection under an Act dealing with this problem. By filing a 'Provisional Specification' inventors' rights were covered for the period of the exhibition. Petitions for patent protection were usually assessed by Law Officers but under the 1851 Act the examination and registration of inventions to be exhibited was delegated to two barristers, both of whom were active members of the Society of Arts – Thomas Webster and Peter Le Neve Foster. (*S of A Jnl.*, Vol.23 (1875), p.665 – Webster *obit.*) Webster and Foster were both Cambridge mathematicians with wide scientific interests. Foster came of a family long associated with the Society and from his election in 1830 he served on many committees including that on 'the Rights of Inventors'; from 1853–79 he was the Society's Secretary. ('Provisional Specifications' for fixed terms were further allowed under the Patent Law Amendment Act 1852 and later legislation to become a constant feature of UK patent practice.)

19 *Ibid.*, preamble.

20 Angus Wilson, *The World of Charles Dickens* (1970), Penguin 1972, p.164.

21 *Household Words*, 19th Oct. 1850. Dickens' 'Poor Man's' application for a patent passed through 35 stages; at para,12, pp.7/8 of the *First Report* (above) a list of 35 stages is set out. Although entitled 'A Recital of the Official Stages …', the *Report's* list is somewhat liberal with its 'stages'. It is hardly a coincidence that Dickens should use this figure of 35; although the *First Report* did not appear in print until 2nd Nov. 1850, Dickens is likely to have seen a copy prior to publication.

22 Dutton, *op.cit.*, p.58. H. Harding, *Patent Office Centenary* (1953), p.7.

[23] *S of A Jnl.*, Vol.I (1852/3), p.3 for Henry Cole's Chairman's Report. Having given the Commissioners three years in which to make a start on putting into effect the requirements of the Act, the Society presented a Memorial urging further action. Points made included the provision of 'proper and suitable buildings' for the new Patent Office, extension of its library with better accommodation for readers, extension of the indexing and classifying of specifications to foreign patents, and 'a judiciously-selected series of models to be collected'. This Memorial was the work of a committee appointed to consider surplus patent fees. It was a 'committee' of formidable size (65 members) and quality. Council authorised the Memorial to be forwarded to the Commissioners on 24 April 1856, simultaneously urging similar action by the British Association and the Institution of Civil Engineers. Little seems to have happened in consequence; despite pressure from many individuals and groups over the next twenty years the Commissioners seemed unwilling or unable to make desired improvements.

[24] *Ibid.*, p.26.

[25] Wood, *op.cit.*, pp.373/4. Also Frank Foden, *The Examiner – James Booth and the origin of common examinations* (1989), pp.63/64.

[26] *S of A Jnl.*, Vol.4 (1855–6), p.1 – James Booth's address; p.41 – Thomas Webster's letter in response. (Provided in full in Appendix IX.) In consequence of disagreements with Webster (who was backed by the majority of the Council), Henry Cole organised an opposition that succeeded in 1850 in turning out Webster and his supporters (Wood, *op.cit.*, pp.359/360). Booth's arrival on the Society of Arts scene during Cole's second term as chairman (an office Webster never attained), the ready acceptance of Booth's ideas by Cole and his friends and Booth's appointment as Chairman of Council only three years after becoming a member of the Society (a position he could not have attained without Cole's support) may account for what may be a hint of acidity in Webster's letter, e.g. 'as an old member of the Society'. Compared with many others Webster was hardly 'an old member' but he had been in membership more than ten years before Booth (his senior in age) appeared.

[27] *S of A Jnl.*, Vol.10, (1861/2), pp.15–16.

[28] Wood, *op.cit.*, pp.336 and 489.

Notes to Chapter 5

[1] Dutton, *op.cit.*, p.60.
[2] *S of A Jnl.*, Vol.1, (1852), p.12.
[3] *6 Vict. cap.V*, Sec.VIII.
[4] Following official printing, the name and chronological indexes (more than 2,000 pages in total) were available to the public in 1854; the subject-matter and reference volumes followed in 1857 and 1855 respectively. The official publication providing 'full particulars' of all patents granted – *The Commissioners of Patents Journal* (later *The Official Journal (Patents)*) – made its first appearance on 7th January, 1854.
[5] *Report of the Commissioners appointed to inquire into ... Letters Patent for Inventions,* 1865, App.A., at pp.147/8 contains extracts from Woodcroft's evidence before the 1849 and 1851 Select Committees.
[6] Richard B. Prosser, 'Bennet Woodcroft, F.R.S.' *The Engineer*, 14 Feby., 1879. This extensive memoir is a mine of information on its subject. More recent studies of Woodcroft are: John Hewish, *The Indefatigable Mr. Woodcroft* (1980), a British Library publication; and Harrison, 'Bennet Woodcroft at the Society of Arts, 1845–57', *RSA Jnl.*, Vol.128 (1980), pp.231–234, 295–298, 375–379.
[7] Gomme, *op.cit.*, p.37.
[8] *Household Words*, 25th February, 1857, pp.190–192. 'A Room near Chancery Lane'. George Dodd was the author of the piece. (Information supplied by John Hewish formerly of the British Library.)
[9] *First Report of the Principles of Jurisprudence* etc. (*S of A* 1850), p.15, *fn*.
[10] *Minutes of the Legislative Committee on the Rights of Inventors*, 12th December, 1850.
[11] *S of A Jnl.*, Vol.1, (1852–3), p.3.
[12] Passage of 1885 report quoted in a paper read to the Society by a former Director of the Science Museum, see *RSA Jnl.*, Vol.61 (1912–13), pp.600 *et seq.*
[13] *S of A Jnl.*, Vol.2 (1853–4), p.101 for Prince Consort's letter to the Society. Harrison, 'Bennet Woodcroft etc.' *op.cit.*, pp.377 and 378 *fn* 22. See also Appendix X.

Notes to Chapter 6

[1] Sir William Armstrong's Presidential Address at the 33rd Meeting of the British Association for the Advancement of Science, held at

Newcastle in 1863; Report, London, 1864, p.liv, (*per* Machlup and Penrose, see note 3 below.)

[2] *The Economist*, July 26, 1851, p.812. This and the succeeding quotation from December 28, 1850 issue of the same journal at p.1434 are taken from Machlup and Penrose below.

[3] Fritz Machlup and Edith Penrose, 'The Patent Controversy in the Nineteenth Century'; *Journal of Economic History*, Vol.X, May 1950, p.22 *fn* 84, p.18, *fn* 66, p.15, ll.4–11.

[4] *S of A Jnl.*, Vol.1 (1852–3), pp.254–6. The Mr. Winkworth mentioned in the quoted passage was very active on the Society's behalf for many years; he worked hard for the 1851 Exhibition (for which Scott Russell was a Commissioner) and served on the Society's Council.

[5] *Ibid.*, Vol.2 (1853–4), p.211.

[6] Wood, *op.cit.*, p.474. It may be that this passage owes something to Trueman Wood having been introduced to the patent situation as an assistant to Bennet Woodcroft at the Patent Office. Woodcroft, generally content with the 1852 reforms, was prepared to admit that detailed improvements could be made but was resistant to many of the more substantial changes canvassed.

[7] *Report of the Royal Commission appointed to inquire into the Working of the Law relating to Patents for Invention*, dated 29th July 1864. Minority reports of W.H. Hindmarch, QC dated 29th September 1864; and William Fairbairn, 15th November 1864. The latter dissented from the majority report on the sole point of the patent term of 14 years; the main report urged no extension, Fairbairn agreed with Hindmarch that where a patentee had not been adequately remunerated prolongation should be granted. The Hindmarch minority report was more extensive and, in retrospect, may be regarded as more useful than that of the majority.

[8] C.D. Abel, *The Action of the Patent Laws in Promoting Invention*, March 1864, p.3. Charles Abel, a Member of the Institution of Mechanical Engineers and an Associate of the Institution of Civil Engineers, practised as a patent agent for fifty years. A foundation member of the Institute of Patent Agents in 1882, he was later Vice-President and President. A member of the Society of Arts, he was awarded the Society's medal for a paper on 'The Patent Laws' in 1904.

[9] The Patent Laws, *Westminster Review*, (1864), Art.IV, pp.322–357, at p.323. This article deals (i) with the Commissioners' Report and (ii) (more extensively) a publication of Robert Andrew Macfie, *The Patent Question: A solution of Difficulties by abolishing or shortening the Inventors' Monopoly*, with a well-reasoned attack on Mr. Macfie's views.

[10] Machlup & Penrose, *op.cit.*, *fn*.76, 'Speech of the Right Hon. Lord Stanley, MP, House of Commons, May 28, 1868. Reproduced in Macfie, ed., *Recent Discussions on the Abolition of Patents for Inventions*, p.111.'

[11] Abel, *op.cit.*, p.38.

[12] *The Times*, 15 July 1891; *Black and White*, 17 August 1898, p.363. *Harding*, *op.cit.*, refers to Patent Office premises and gives details of the stages of re-building, pp.33–36. Evidence of where building broke off in 1912 never to be recommenced was still evident at the end of the twentieth century.

[13] Harding, *op.cit.*, p.38.

[14] House of Commons Sessional Papers 1864; Special Committee on the Patent Office Library and Museum; Q/As 1470 and 1613. At Q/A 1470 Webster continued in his answer by further references to lack of Patent Office accommodation, echoing some points from the Society of Arts' Memorial to the Commissioners in 1856 (see *S of A Jnl.*, Vol.1, 1852–3, p.3): 'The provisional specifications cannot be seen, and therefore nobody knows what is being applied for; that is quite contrary to the spirit of the Act, and to remedy it would require another class of offices, that is to say, rooms for inspecting those provisional specifications ... then comes the larger question of offices for the public library and reading rooms, and what I call either the model or the exhibition room; I use that word advisedly, rather than the word "museum"'.

[15] The background to the 'Clerk of the Patents' position in and departure from the Patent Office has been succinctly told by Harding in his *Patent Office Centenary* at pp.16–21; more fully related by one of Harding's colleagues, V.G. Alexander, in the *Journal of the Institute of Public Administration*, (Winter, 1950) No.28 at p.298 *et seq*; and from a different angle by J.C. Sainty, a former Reading Clerk in the House of Lords, in the *Journal of the Chartered Institute of Patent Agents*, (Nov, 1983) pp.38–45. Notwithstanding these references the temptation to relate some features of the saga is irresistible: A John Edmunds lost his life in 1826 while canvassing as election agent for Henry Brougham. Brougham sought to provide for the Edmunds' children and articled son Leonard to a London solicitor. On becoming Lord Chancellor Brougham found a couple of lucrative official places for Leonard which he was able to replace in 1833–4 with more permanent offices. These were 'Clerk of the Patents', concerned with invention patents, and 'Clerk of the Crown in Chancery', concerned with patents of creation and appointment. Leonard Edmunds later came to an arrangement with another Brougham, a Master in Chancery,

whereby he surrendered the 'Clerk of the Crown' office in favour of the more remunerative position of 'Reading Clerk in the House of Lords'. His 1852 appointment as 'Clerk to the Commissioners of Patents' brought his annual income from public funds to £2,500. (Woodcroft's £1,000 a year salary would have been regarded as a handsome income at that time. Edmunds, incidentally, lived rent-free at the Brougham town residence.) Edmunds' deputy as 'Clerk of the Patents', Thomas Ruscoe, became effective head of the Patent Division of the new Office and handled ever-increasing patent fees that rose to substantial sums as patent applications increased. Ruscoe's book-keeping methods were somewhat unusual. He 'banked' through an uncle with business premises adjoining the Patent Office, the uncle booking in patent fees under the heading 'Tom's Account'. When a disagreement with Woodcroft led to reference to the Commissioners, followed by an Inquiry into Patent Office affairs by a pair of legal gentlemen, careful probings stirred muddy waters. The outcome was a mid-Victorian 'soap' that had the reading public entertained with its unexpected twists, turns and complexities for twenty years. When Leonard Edmunds first acquired a 'property' in an official position (1830) it is unlikely that anyone would have shown undue concern at small parcels of public funds finding their way into a private purse (perquisites of office, surely); fifty years later when Edmunds was still fighting his corner such transactions had begun to have the taint of criminality. The outcome of 'the Edmunds affair' affected more than Patent Office staff and practices, among the more far-reaching consequences was that book-keeping in public departments was never quite the same again.

16 R.B. Prosser, *The Engineer*, *op.cit.* Prior to taking up the Patent Office appointment Woodcroft had a succession of business and invention interests. Following a brief partnership with his father he appears to have run a business of his own as a textile manufacturer. After a patent related to dyeing had provided him with a small fortune he sold it for a comparatively minor sum. Then he applied himself over a long period to problems of marine screw propulsion during which period he also developed a weaving loom with many novel features. About 1837/8 he moved from Manchester, site of a silk manufacturing business he had started, to Oldham where his fustian loom seems for a time to have been his principal concern. By 1845 he was back in Manchester as a consulting engineer and, it would seem, a patent agent. Three years later he was in London as a consulting engineer, leaving his able junior partner in Manchester to build up a successful and enduring patent agency. He was appointed Professor of Machinery at University College,

London, early in 1847, a post for which he was totally unsuited and which he neglected in order to continue his marine propulsion interests. His entry to the 'temporary' premises of the new Patent Office came on or near to his forty-ninth birthday and, for the first time in approximately thirty years of business/professional experience, he was not in sole control of matters for which he was responsible. He threw himself into the publication of patent indexes and abridgments and the formation of a library with enthusiasm; if he lost interest in these tedious matters after a few years, it would be in keeping with the pattern of his earlier life. As with the Manchester patent agency, he found very able subordinates to superintend the day to day work of the Specification Division and of the Library. He does not appear ever to have lost interest in the 'Patent Museum'. His memorial biographer wrote, 'Those who knew Mr. Woodcroft could not fail to be aware of his strong antiquarian bias, and it is not surprising that it should have shown itself in the collection of objects illustrative of the history of his favourite pursuits.' When addressing the Society of Arts in 1913, a former Director of the Science Museum commended Woodcroft for his contribution to his museum's collection: 'Many of the most treasured elements of the collections as they now stand were brought together in the Patent Office Museum . . . The nation, and indeed the world, owes a debt to Mr. Bennet Woodcroft for his watchful, keen and well-directed activity in securing for this collection many machines of prime importance in the history of invention'. A worthy tribute, but if meritorious antiquarian zeal was at the cost of degradation of patent indexes and abridgments many engaged in patents had cause for complaint.

[17] Mid-seventeenth century epitaph to Sir Robert Shirley, Bt., Staunton Harold, Leicestershire.

Notes to Chapter 7

[1] A very readable account of changes in Civil Service structure is provided in a pamphlet produced on the occasion of the centenary of the publication of the Northcote-Trevelyan Report – *The British Civil Service 1854–1954*, Wyn Griffith, HMSO. The Report remained for the most part in limbo until 1868 onwards. An Order in Council of 1870 'marked the beginning of the end of the patronage system . . . the sitting tenants were numerous and powerful, and some of them were not enthusiastic about the new methods'.

2 Wood, 'Registration of Trade Marks', *S of A Jnl.*, Vol.24, (1875–6), pp.17–31 and 49–54.

3 Wood, 'The Patents for Invention Bill, 1877', *S of A Jnl.*, Vol.25 (1876–7), pp.339–348.

4 Peter Le Neve Foster (1809–1879), Secretary of the Society of Arts from 1853 to 1879 was of a family associated with the Society from the eighteenth through to the twentieth century. His own membership dated from 1837 and for more than forty years he rendered tremendous service. Close in age to Thomas Webster their early careers ran parallel; after reading mathematics at Cambridge he was called to the Bar (1836) and practised until becoming Secretary to the Society. He took a full share in the 1840s re-organisation of the Society with Webster, following which, again with Webster, he oversaw the carrying into effect of the Act for the Protection of Inventions prior to and during the 1851 Exhibition. In addition, he was involved in preparatory work for that exhibition as a treasurer and was even more closely connected with the Exhibition of 1862. His scientific interests were wide, for example, he gave talks at the Society of Arts on such diverse subjects as 'Aluminium' and 'Figure Weaving by Electricity'; he was also a founder member of the Photographic Society. In addition to being an office-holder and regular attender at meetings of the British Association for the Advancement of Science, he was also a corresponding member of several foreign societies, including the Netherlands Society for the Promotion of Inventions. – *S of A Jnl.*, Vol.27 (1878–9), pp.316–7 and Wood, *op.cit.*, pp.364–6.

5 'The British Association owed its origin in part to Brewster's distress about the state of patent law. Brewster was the frustrated, impecunious inventor of the kaleidoscope. He called for an association to redress "that vicious and fraudulent legislation" which "places the most exalted officers of State in the position of a legalized banditti, who stab the inventor through the folds of an Act of Parliament, and rifle him in the presence of the Lord Chief Justice ..." The 1831 meeting [the first general meeting of the Association] showed signs of responding to Brewster's concerns'. The inaugural speech made reference to the protection of inventions and urged reform of the patent laws. 'Invention, technological progress, and the mechanical and chemical arts lay within the domain of the British Association from the very start'. However, personality problems and a strong academic bias in the new Association resulted in technology and the mechanical and chemical arts taking subordinate positions. As a consequence,

'patent law reform was not even considered until the late 1850s'. So concerned were the early 'Gentlemen of Science' (i.e. the promoters of the B.A.A.S.) to avoid being contaminated by the practical arts that the Association's original Mechanical Arts' Sub-committee barely survived into a second year, but in 1836 there was a change of heart and the Sub-committee was upgraded to become the Mechanical Science Committee and a component of the Association's Section G. 'Section G brought together university teachers and practical men, with the former in firm control. The senior office holders were most often academics ... The academics were absent from the lowlier secretariat of the Section; here practising engineers and an employee of the Institution of Civil Engineers (Thomas Webster) were dominant'. Benjamin Rotch, barrister, inventor, patents advisor and Vice-President of the Society of Arts was involved in discussions preceding the 1831 Inaugural Meeting to which he contributed a paper but appears to have lost interest soon afterwards (became a 'sleeping partner'!). A few Society of Arts people were appointed Vice-Presidents of the Mechanical Science Committee in the period 1838–44 (the Committee was near extinction in 1845–7) including Bryan Donkin (sometime Chairman of the Society's Committee of Mechanics and Vice-President), William Fairbairn and John Scott Russell. In 1837 and 1838 Thomas Webster was a Secretary of the Committee along with the railway engineer C.B. Vignolles; in 1839 Webster again served in this capacity, this time with William Carpmael and another; in 1840 Russell and Vignolles shared the secretariat; in 1841 it was Webster and another; 1841 Russell and Vignolles; 1844 Webster and Vignolles (Russell was Vice-President in that year). Russell was later to become quite a significant figure in the Association as the recipient of very considerable financial assistance for his researches into the effects of wave motion on hull construction. 'Engineers and manufacturers were harnessed to the Association's wider purposes. Their goodwill was invaluable in arranging exciting spectacles at Association Meetings, such as ... the exhibitions of manufactures and inventions, beginning with that at Newcastle in 1838. ... The apotheosis of these Association-pioneered exhibitions occurred in 1851 with the Great Exhibition at the Crystal Palace in London'. The Society of Arts received official notice of the Association's 1831 Inaugural Meeting, as did its Secretary Arthur Aikin, though in a personal capacity as an Honorary Member of the Yorkshire Philosophical Society. The Duke of Sussex, President of the Society, also received an invitation but replied with a double-barrelled negative. Only a year earlier the Duke as President of the Royal Society had favoured a conservative element in that Society against a vigorous reform group that included some who went on to found the British Association. (His reverse role at the Society of Arts in 1842/3 was greatly to the benefit of the Society). Tensions between the 'Gentlemen of Science' coterie and the Duke (and other Royal Society elements) may have affected briefly relations between the British Association and the Society of Arts but the over-riding differentiating element lay in the Association's 'vision of proper science' to which the practical arts were subservient. Abstracted from Jack Morrell and Arnold Thackray, *Gentlemen of Science – Early Years of the British Association for the Advancement of Science* (1981), with reference primarily to pp.256–7 and 262–5.

6 Sir Frederick Augustus Abel (1827–1900), chemist, authority on explosives and joint inventor of 'Cordite', received the Society's Albert Medal (awarded annually for 'Distinguished Merit in Promoting Arts, Manufactures or Commerce') in 1891 with regard to 'several important classes of Arts and Manufactures ... and especially by his researches in the manufacture of iron and steel ... and in acknowledgment of the great services he has rendered to the State ... as Chemist to the War Department'. After acting as organising secretary during preliminary work he became the Imperial Institute's first Director. He was President of the British Association's Chemistry Committee in 1887 after being Chairman of Council of the Society of Arts 1883–4. *D.N.B.* and Wood, *History, op.cit.*, p.515.

7 Sir Charles William Siemens (1823–1883) was born in Hanover, one of eight brothers. Though not within the usual context of 'necessity being the mother of invention' their story could be so regarded. The death of their father when most brothers were fairly young left the eldest, Werner, then a Prussian officer trained in the engineer and artillery school at Berlin, responsible for their upbringing. He urged those who would to take up technical education to a high standard. The outcome was a stream of outstanding inventions. William came to England in 1843 to find a purchaser for an electroplating process and was markedly successful. Returning the following year with two quite different inventions which proved more difficult to dispose of, he attracted the interest of a Midlands manufacturer who offered employment and William decided to settle. Even without this offer he may have settled, for in doing so he fitted in with family business arrangements. Werner created an extensive electrical engineering empire in Germany while brother Karl saw to the development of family inventions – and his own industrial concerns – in Russia. Meanwhile one of the inventions William brought to England in

1844 was successfully exploited, after some twelve years of experimentation and development, as a major industrial fuel-saving arrangement. The UK patent for this was taken out in the name of brother Frederick. In 1850 William received the Society of Arts' gold medal for a 'regenerative condenser' (patents 12,006 of 1847 and 12,531 of 1849). The invention was not an immediate commercial success but many years afterwards, when Chairman of Council, Siemens said that this prize, the first he had ever received, had been of the greatest encouragement to him. This invention gave rise to the 'regenerative furnace' which by its capacity greatly to reduce fuel consumption proved to be of immense value to the steel and glass industries. Siemens received the Society's Albert Medal in 1874 'For his researches in connection with the laws of heat, and the practical applications of them to furnaces used in the Arts; and for his improvements in the manufacture of iron; and generally for the services rendered by him in connection with the economisation of fuel in its various applications to Manufactures and the Arts'. Siemens was elected a member of the Society in 1849 on the proposal of Thomas Webster and was Chairman of Council in 1882. He became a member of the Institution of Civil Engineers in 1860, a Fellow of the Royal Society two years later, President of the Mechanical Science Committee of the British Association in 1869 and of the British Association itself in 1882. – Sources: *D.N.B.*; Wood, *History, op.cit.*, p.513 (for Albert Medal); Chairman's Address, *S of A Jnl.*, Vol.31 (1882–3) pp.6–13.

8 *Engineering*, 8 August 1873, p.106.

9 I.J.G. Davis and J. Harrison, 'Prelude to the United Kingdom's Accession to the Paris Convention, March 17, 1884', *Industrial Property*, November, 1984, pp.395–399.

10 Richard Webster (1842–1915), Attorney-General on three occasions (twelve years in total), was appointed Lord Chief Justice in 1910, he had previously been a member of a committee appointed by the Board of Trade in 1885 to 'Inquire into the Duties etc.' of the Patent Office (the 'Herschell Committee') and of another Government-appointed body in 1900 commissioned to consider problems of patent applications for inventions that were manifestly old. Member of Council of the Society of Arts, Chairman 1890–93, President 1910–11 (as Alveston L.C.J.).

11 For Professor Neumann's observations see *Engineering*, 15 August, 1873, p.126. According to Machlup and Penrose, *op.cit.*, p.4 including (first) *fn*.8; 'At the annual meeting of the Kongress deutscher Volkswirthe held in Dresden, September, 1863, the following resolution was adopted "by an overwhelming majority":

"Considering that patents hinder rather than further the progress of invention; that they hamper the prompt general utilisation of useful inventions; that on balance they cause more harm than benefit to the inventors themselves and, thus, are a highly deceptive form of compensation; the Congress of German Economists resolves that patents of invention are injurious to common welfare"'. ... 'After several years of public discussion, the government of Prussia decided to oppose the adoption of a patent law by the North German Federation, and in December, 1868 Chancellor Bismark announced his objections to the principle of patent protection.' During the Vienna Congress of 1873 Karl Pieper, a Civil Engineer from Dresden who acted as Secretary to the Congress, made mention of the patent systems of America and England 'with the patent legislation of which countries that of Prussia contrasted most unfavourably, as being the worst in existence, in practice and application'. (See *Engineering*, 15 August, 1873, p.126.) Following Trueman Wood's paper on 'The Patents for Inventions Bill, 1877' on 6 March, 1877 (*S of A Jnl.*, Vol.25, pp.339–348), Karl Pieper took part in the discussion saying, *inter alia*, 'Prussia never had a Patent-law, but a kind of king's order had been issued in 1815, and since then certain officials had exercised the power of granting patents. For many years the principle acted upon had been that things which would be of great benefit to the public should not be patented, from the idea that it would be a hindrance to industry, but now a sounder opinion prevailed and it was seen that to protect invention was to benefit the public. There was now a law before the German Parliament very similar to the English, and in some points superior to it'.

12 Wood, *History, etc.*, *op.cit.*, p.464. W.H.G. Armytage, *A Social History of Engineering* (1961), pp.238 and 240. Armytage also mentions earlier moves in the direction of technical education, such as John Scott Russell's 1869 call for technical colleges in industrial towns to provide a *corps d'élite* on the French model, and the Society of Arts' establishment of the country's first technical examinations under the encouragement of John Donnelly, a member of its Council. Donnelly arranged for these examinations to be taken over by a committee incorporated in 1880 as the City and Guilds of London Institute for the Advancement of Technical Education. These represent but a few of the proposals and developments relating to technical education. In his passages on technical education Armytage makes particular reference to Bernhard Samuelson and A.J. Mundella ('familiar names'). Samuelson, a great advocate for technical education which he had studied on the Continent, was an *entrepreneur extraordinaire* with a wide range of business interests

in Britain and overseas. He was also interested in patents, chaired a Select Committee of the House of Commons on the patent system, 1871–2 and was a member of the 'Herschell Committee' 1885–6. Mundella, a member of the Society's Council, also had overseas business interests though in his case they appear to have been limited to a branch factory of his Midlands hosiery concern. This off-shoot factory was located in Chemnitz where Mundella took a great interest in the local education facilities. Under the 1880 Gladstone government he was Vice-President of a Committee of the Privy Council for Education. During the sittings of the Board of Trade Inquiry into the Patent Office (the 'Herschell Committee') in 1886 he was President of the Board of Trade. At the Society of Arts he participated in patent discussions, speaking at length in the debate following Wood's 1877 paper on the Patents Bill of that year. (He also chaired the meeting in 1875 at which Wood gave a paper 'On the Registration of Trade Marks'.)

13 Frederick Bramwell, 'The Society of Arts Patent Bill, and some points in American patent law and practice bearing thereon', *S of A Jnl.*, Vol.31 (1882–3), pp.285–299 at pp.286/7.

14 Sir William Henry Perkin (1838–1907) received the Society's Albert Medal for 'the method of obtaining colouring matter from coal tar, a discovery which led to the establishment of a new and important industry'. Perkin was a student at the Royal College of Chemistry when he made this discovery. In 1845 Prince Albert had invited a distinguished German chemist, August Wilhelm von Hofmann to become the first Superintendent of the College and Hofmann had found a way of making aniline cheaply from coal tar. Perkin, experimenting with aniline, discovered the dye first known as 'aniline purple' (later as 'mauve' or 'mauvine') in 1856 and took out a patent. In 1869 he perfected a method of synthesising alizarine – the colouring component of madder – and thereby put the synthetic dyestuff industry on a firm footing (and simultaneously ruined European madder growers). Again he applied for a patent, only to find he had been beaten to the UK Patent Office by a couple of days or so. German chemists had also appreciated the importance of alizarine and had put more resources into the work than were at Perkin's disposal. (See Wood, *History, etc., op.cit.*, p.514 for Albert Medal citation; also to be noted A.W. Hofmann's Albert Medal in 1881 when he was 'Professor of chemistry at the University of Berlin'. For brief reference to Perkin see, e.g. T.K. Derry and Trevor I. Williams, *A Short History of Technology* (1960), pp.543–546.

15 D.N.B. and Wood, *History etc., op.cit.*, pp.447 and 475/6.

16 *S of A Jnl.*, Vol.23 (1874–5), pp.34–48.

17 *S of A Jnl.*, Vol.27 (1878–9), pp.517–527; Vol.30 (1881–82), pp.6–15; Vol.31 (1882–3), pp.285–299.

18 *S of A Jnl.*, Vol.31 (1882–3), p.565. Richard Webster's observation regarding the abolition of 'the Commissioners of Patents as a body' was made when he opened a discussion on 20 April, 1883, on the Government's Patent Bill then before the House of Commons. The meeting had heard a paper read by Trueman Wood setting out the main elements of the Bill; Wood acknowledged the assistance received from Frederick Bramwell and Alfred Carpmael in the preparation of this paper. The following passage appeared in the paper (p.558): 'The tone of the able speech in which the Bill was introduced by the President of the Board of Trade, showed that he was seriously anxious to promote a reform of the law, and that he had given full attention to the views which have been put forward in this room both by the Chairman of the Council, Sir William Siemens, and by his immediate predecessor, Sir Frederick Bramwell. I think, therefore, that there is every reason to believe that he will be ready to listen to the opinions which may be expressed in the discussion of this evening, and that the Society of Arts, whose work has already been so well appreciated, may render yet further service to the Government in the difficult task of introducing a new patent system.' In opening discussion Richard Webster said 'he could not but recognise that this Bill was a great gain to the inventive mind of the country, and whatever might be its defects, it would be a lamentable thing if the year went by without its being passed. It was very gratifying to see that the discussion whether patents were desirable at all, seemed to have entirely subsided, and the only question now remaining was, as to the best system of Patent-law to be adopted. He should have, in many points, to compare the provisions of the Society of Arts' Bill with that now brought forward by the Government, not for the purpose of suggesting that the Society should endeavour simply to force its views on Parliament, but because he thought a careful examination of the two would show that the framers of the Society's Bill had studied the subject more carefully, and had thought out their views more thoroughly than those who had framed the Government Bill. He did not say there were no points in which the Government Bill was to be preferred, but in the most important and difficult matters, the Society's Bill was, in his judgment, undoubtedly superior.' He continued with the passage quoted in the main text.

19 Another break with Medieval practice had taken effect by adminis-

trative action before 1883. The engrossing of Letters Patent on large skins of parchment to which the Great Seal was applied pendant from cords continued until 1878 when a wafer seal was substituted for the wax one. In 1884 the wafer seal of the Patent Office replaced the wafer of the Great Seal and parchment was replaced by paper, Gomme, *op.cit.*, p.40. Consequent on the replacement of the wax Great Seal by a wafer, it was no longer necessary for clerks of the Lord Chancellor's office to journey to their superiors' residences (sometimes in the Scottish highlands) during vacations, encumbered with a great many pounds avoirdupois of wax and parchment so that formal sealing could take place in the presence of the Lord Chancellor, nor did busy barristers who had represented parties in court at revocation proceedings have to wait on the Lord Chancellor's pleasure in order to be present as the cord was snipped severing the Great Seal from its associated parchment which thereby ceased to be Letters Patent.

20 Harding, *op.cit.*, pp.29, 36–7.

21 Eric Robinson and A.E. Musson, *James Watt and the Steam Revolution* (1969), p.213.

22 Wood, *History*, *op.cit.*, pp.474–7, more particularly at p.476; Harding, *op.cit.*, p.28.

23 There appears to have been something of a hiatus in the Society's patent discussions in the mid 1870s. In his 1876 Chairman's Address Lord Alfred Spencer Churchill had quite a lot to say about the patent situation, including the following illuminating observations: 'The recent attempts to alter the existing Patent system have been carefully watched by the Council, and if they have not asked the Society to join them in considering the proposed alterations, it is only because they believe that, by the reports of successive Commissions, as well as the discussions which have taken place at the numerous meetings which have been held during the last few years here and elsewhere, the subject has been so thoroughly ventilated that no real good can result from any further discussion. ... Numerous as are the objectors, and loud as are their complaints, it yet remains to be shown that any pressing necessity for reform – that is to say, legislative reform – exists at all. That there is much room for improvement in the administration of the Patent-office is beyond a doubt. ... Seeing much need for administrative reform, though none for legal, the Council have determined to memorialise the Lord Chancellor, asking him to abstain from further attempts at legislation.' (*S of A Jnl.*, Vol.25 (1876–7), pp.11–12.) Correlation of judgment and phrasing with passages in Wood's *History* (p.474) may not be coincidental: 'After 1852 ... the question of Patent Law reform was for a long time

allowed to slumber ... the criticisms of objectors were mainly directed to matters of detail, which might perfectly well have been dealt with by administrative rather than legal reform.' In the light of Lord Alfred's passage 'no real good can result from any further discussion', the opening words of Trueman Wood's paper on 'The Patents for Inventions Bill, 1877' take on a singularly curious interest, 'The Council of this Society have honoured me with their instructions to prepare a paper which might serve to introduce the subject for this evening's discussion.' Was it coincidence that 'The Patent Law Committee, 1875', which met in the Council Room of the Institution of Civil Engineers under the chairmanship of William Siemens, came into being about the time of this period of apparent restricted discussion at the Society? Among the forty or so people associated with the Society in this group were its Secretary, Peter Le Neve Foster, Henry Cole, Lyon Playfair and Thomas Webster. (See Appendix XIII).

24 *S of A Jnl.*, Vol.31 (1882–3), p.6.

Notes to Chapter 8

1 Henry Reader Lack was appointed to be the first Registrar of Trade Marks in December, 1875 and in March, 1876 became Clerk to the Commissioners of Patents on the 'retirement' of Bennet Woodcroft. A resumé of his career is given in 'The Society of Arts and Trade Marks Registration' (Harrison, *RSA. Jnl.*, Vol. 124 (1976), at p.148, note 20). It was during Lack's attendance at an international conference on patents prior to the Paris Convention of 1883 that the style 'Comptroller-General of Patents' (rather than 'Clerk to the Commissioners') appears to have been used for the first time. Reader Lack was of a family having long and extensive Board of Trade connexions. His father, Edward John, was on the staff of the Board from 1816 to about 1848. (He also received a certificate of appointment to the Customs Service in 1831.) Edward John had married a cousin one branch of whose family had a noble pedigree. Henry Reader, the son and future Comptroller, also married a cousin whose father, Richard, was also in the Board's employ – from 1827 to 1867. Richard's father, in his turn, had been at the Board. He had held a position corresponding to that of a present-day Permanent Secretary from 1810–1836, following more junior positions from 1786 and a period as personal secretary to Lord Liverpool. There were other Lacks scattered around government offices. (Information taken from

J.C. Sainty, *Office Holders in Modern Britain*, Vol. III, 'Officials of the Board of Trade, 1660 –1870', and family records provided by Mr. Henry Charles Lack, for whose kindness the present writer is indebted.) An interesting, if purely entertaining, interposition with reference to this period relates to the further activities of the writer of 'A Poor Man's Tale of a Patent'. Midway through the Lack era at the Board, Charles Dickens took a leading part in the formation of 'The Administrative Reform Society' in an outburst of exasperation with a government that appeared indifferent to socials ills, to which had been added blatant inefficiency and muddle during the Crimean War. Again the reforming pen had scribbled quickly, serialisation of 'Hard Times' began early in 1854 in *Household Words* and of 'Little Dorrit' at the end of 1855. In 'Little Dorrit' administrators were pilloried. 'Chapter 10 – Containing the whole Science of Government' is bitter: 'The Barnacle family had for some time helped to administer the Circumlocution Office ... The Barnacles were a very high family, and a very large family. They were dispersed all over the public offices ...' Because of blocking tactics of the Barnacles, Daniel Doyce, inventor but not a poor man (patents are not mentioned) can only market his products abroad – more especially in Russia! Too readily in later years the 'Circumlocution Office' was equated with the Patent Office – most unlikely since during the serialisation of 'Little Dorrit' *Household Words* simultaneously printed 'A Room in Chancery Lane', a piece eulogizing the staff of the Patent Office. If any specific department of state was in the pillory (and, after all, it was the government's administrative machine as a whole that was really under attack) and, having in mind that Doyce's difficulties seem to have been in respect of the marketing of his goods, it is the Board of Trade that would seem to have been in the firing line.

2 With overall administration in the hands of legal gentlemen (the Commissioners of Patents) primarily occupied with the numerous functions normally falling within the purview of such officers of state as these were, Bennet Woodcroft could oversee the Patent Office as if it were his personal fiefdom. In consequence, this seigneur did not take kindly to a judicious suggestion that the time had come for his suzerainty to pass to other hands. With engineering periodicals leaning to 'Old Woodcroft' and unhappy that the Office had fallen into the hands of a bureaucrat lacking technical expertise, Woodcroft's successor did not have a good press, but there were also practical problems. A plaintive message from the South Kensington outstation to headquarters signalled present and future trouble. It was to the effect that 'a horse-drawn wagon

arrived, the carter said he had instructions from Mr. Woodcroft to take the Symington marine engine to Mr. Woodcroft's residence.' This was but a hint of things to come. Over many years Woodcroft, who in this respect appears to have been remarkably silver-tongued, had persuaded owners of old engineering artefacts and models to pass them into his personal care. To whom did they belong in 1876? That question was not settled in Woodcroft's lifetime. His widow, thirty years younger and a battle-axe reared on an Elstree farm, carried on to her death a campaign for public reimbursement of artefacts etc. acquired by and regarded as the personal property of her late husband. It is unlikely that at the end of a long period of torment for several public officials and/or authorities the South Kensington museum lost many, if any, of the 'Patent Museum' artefacts, though whether any of the 'Engineering Models and Portraits (Recently exhibited at South Kensington' – as an auctioneers' 1903 catalogue proclaimed them) were purchased by the museum is not known. The 'Gallery of Portraits of Inventors' appears to have suffered more, it was dispersed following this 1903 auction.

3 *Minutes of Evidence of the Committee of Inquiry into the Duties, etc. of the Patent Office* ('Herschell Committee'), *1886*. H.T. Wood's evidence, 8th May 1886, pp.45–48; Questions 888, 909 and 918 referred to in main text. It is probable that few outsiders would know more of Patent Office matters than Trueman Wood. Presumably, while serving as Secretary of the Society of Arts he made frequent visits to the Patent Office taking the abridgments he had prepared and coming away with specifications to be abridged. He would be acquainted with many of the senior staff, including Richard Bissell Prosser, son of the Richard Prosser who had served on the Society's patent committees in the early 1850s. Contacts between Wood and R.B. Prosser were maintained over a long period. Most of Wood's abridging work was done under the heading 'Agricultural Field Implements', but he occasionally worked on other subject-matter.

4 Ecclesiasticus 44, ll.8 and 9 (NEB).

5 Harrison, 'Some Patent Practitioners etc.,' *RSA Jnl., op.cit.,* Vol. 130.

6 Harding, *op.cit.*, pp.31–32.

7 Abel, 'The Patent Laws', *S of A Jnl.,* Vol.53 (1904–5), pp.82–101. The lecturer received the Society's gold medal. By the time of this lecture Charles Denton Abel had had a long career in patents. It is probable that he was not unacquainted with them when he entered into partnership with a consulting engineer and patent agent in 1856 during the surge of patent applications consequent

on the entry into force of the 1852 Act. The pamphlet he prepared and caused to be printed at the time of the 1863/4 Royal Commission (mentioned in the main text) contained many wise observations and suggestions. A founder member of the Institute of Patent Agents, he served terms as Vice-President and President; his later partner, John Imray, was President in 1886 and presented the Institute's case to the Herschell Committee requesting that patent agency be treated as 'a close profession like solicitors or others'. Charles Abel's talk was followed by a discussion in which a new generation of patent agents took part, but a few representatives of the heroic age of patent reform were present. Sir William Lloyd Wise offered an observation and Sir Alexander Siemens made an extensive contribution quoting his father in support of views that no inventor would wish to hear, such as, 'Patent laws are not for the benefit of the inventor, they are really for the man who carries out an invention. ... It is not the man who invents the thing but the man who introduces it to the public who should benefit. ... The real value of an invention is its adoption. ... Generally the manufacturer knows more about the thing than the inventor himself'. Here we catch a glimpse of the perennial tension between inventors, manufacturers, capitalists and, of course, public benefit. Abel's evening closed a chapter at the Society. Hitherto the Society had provided a neutral ground where all with interests in innovation and with encouragement of practical arts and manufactures could express opinions but these general debates ceased to be attractive in a period of specialization when each particular group was concerned to discuss matters solely from its own viewpoint. Patents had become a very esoteric subject.

Notes to Chapter 9

1 Wood, *History, op.cit.*, p.343.

2 See extensive extracts from Morrell and Thackray, *Gentlemen of Science* at note 5, Chapter 7. From the same source other extracts further indicate the inferior position of the practical arts in the thinking of the academically-based dominant group of the early British Association: 'The Gentlemen of Science were a particular, partisan group ... Their bases of power lay in Cambridge and in the Geological and Astronomical Societies ... Their rhetoric always stressed the objective, shared nature of scientific enterprise. At the same time their message was congruent with latent or overt hostil-

ity to participation on equal terms by women, workers, provincials, or professionals not committed to gentlemanly voluntarism. Their rhetoric, in fact, served their own intellectual and career interests' (p.28). 'The subsidiary place of technology was again revealed in the nature of the lobbies of Government mounted by the BAAS; in the absence of engineering from the managerial core of the Association; and in the near extinction of Section G between 1845 and 1847. With respect to lobbies, the personal interests of the Gentlemen of Science meant that such an obvious candidate as patent law reform was not even considered until the late 1850s' (p.265).

[3] Wood, *History, op.cit.*, pp.346/7.

[4] Wood in his *History, op.cit.*, (p.346 *fn*) makes specific mention of a few people associated with Thomas Webster in the reform of the Society: 'Edward Speer, George Bailey, J. Scott Russell (the eminent engineer, afterwards Secretary), John Bethell, Joseph Woods (architect, geologist and botanist) and William Tooke (solicitor)'. At p.361 he adds 'Sir W.H. Bodkin, the eminent lawyer'. Of these Russell and Woods were not members before 1843, though both served the Society well later. Wood's list does not include three very probable supporters:- Benjamin Rotch (barrister), Edward Solly (chemist) and Thomas Winkworth (silk broker). W.H. Bodkin proposed Peter Le Neve Foster (barrister and later Secretary) for membership in 1837; it is reasonable to assume that Webster also had Le Neve Foster's backing. All these people were to perform sterling work for the Society later. Edward Speer became the first Chairman of Council, an office he later shared with George Bailey (architect) who had been a member from 1821.

[5] *Proceedings of the Institution of Civil Engineers,* Vol.16 (1856–7), pp.143–150. The relevant passage reads: 'Perhaps the greatest of Mr. Whishaw's public services was the direction of his energies to the resuscitation of the Society of Arts, which would probably have died a natural death, had he not opportunely assembled a few influential men who afforded him their support as Secretary in his highly meritorious and successful task, for the accomplishment of which he is fairly entitled to great praise. About the end of the year 1842, it was seriously contemplated to break up the Society, and a resolution was passed, though never acted upon, to the effect that the funds were no longer sufficient to retain the services of a salaried Secretary. It was under these circumstances that Mr. Whishaw entered upon the duties of that office. He was very energetic and successful in personally canvassing for members, inducing one hundred and forty new members to join within a few

months; and he at once introduced improvements in the character of the evening meetings, by obtaining and contributing Papers for discussion. These efforts, combined with the alterations in the general principles and management of the Society, introduced by other Members, who began to take an interest in it, may be said to have laid the foundation of its present prosperity.' The specific statement in this Memoir 'inducing one hundred and forty new members to join within a few months' evokes speculation that this was a figure totted up by Whishaw in the bitterness of later years as he reflected on his treatment at the hands of certain members of the Society. The notice in the Society's *Journal* of its former Secretary's death refers only to his activities to 1845: 'It is to the zeal and energy of Mr. Whishaw that the Society stands indebted in a great measure for its resuscitation. He accepted the office of Secretary at a time when there were few members to support his exertions, and scarcely any funds with which to meet its expenditure. Owing to his continued personal efforts, backed by the advice and assistance of a few active members whom he gathered around him, he succeeded in instilling new life into the then all but expiring body. His labours to improve the character of the Society's evening meetings, the *conversazioni* he established, and the efforts he made to promote the formation of a National Exhibition of the Industries of Great Britain, brought around him a body of friends and members who, on his retiring from the office in 1845, elected him an Honorary Life Member of the Society.'

Other obituary notices indicate reasons why Whishaw may have had cause to feel bitter regarding his experiences relative to the Society after 1845, as detailed in the following extracts from a long tribute to him in *The Civil Engineer and Architects' Journal*, to which the present author's attention was drawn by his friend and former colleague Dr. R.T. Smith: 'It was in connection with the Society of Arts that Mr. Whishaw's public services were best known. Having accepted the Secretaryship of that Society when it was at a very low ebb, he laid the basis for its present prosperity, and gave the example of special exhibitions; under his liberal and energetic management the *conversaziones* became occasions of *réunion* for the leading professors of science and art. . . . His desire to promote the industrial arts led him to devise the plan for the Exhibition of all Nations, in which he received the countenance and co-operation of his Royal Highness Prince Albert, Mr. Robert Stephenson, and others, but in the prosperity of which he found himself, by an intrigue, deprived of all employment and rightful acknowledgment. The committee was first held at the Society of Arts, and afterwards in Gray's-inn. Mr. Thomas Winkworth, the political economist, was the author of the plan of extending the Exhibition to all nations. Mr. Robert Stephenson liberally contributed to the funds, and may be considered virtually as the mainstay of the scheme of the Exhibition. Mr. Whishaw was solely employed as a local commissioner for a short time in the beginning, and received a small pecuniary grant at the close. ... The vexation he felt from the treatment to which he was exposed, and some very heavy pecuniary losses, seriously undermined his health for the last few years of his life. ... He was lately employed in promoting a museum of patent inventions [the Patent Museum], which, under the patronage of his friend, Sir John Romilly, the Master of the Rolls, he hoped would have allowed him, even in his inferior state of health, to be of service to the public.

In personal character Francis Whishaw was esteemed for great parts and probity, but his integrity was so unflinching that it earned him many enemies. Independent in his bearing, confident in his integrity, he was a fierce foe to quackery in science and quacks in morals; and as this was marked by some asperity of character, the quacks at length got the better of him. Ousted by intrigues or overcome by toadies and lickspittles, it was easy to represent that Whishaw was uncertain in his temper, unstable in his disposition, and at length that he was an impracticable man; though he was undoubtedly a good servant to those who employed him, a good master to those under him, and a good colleague to those who acted with him. The Great Exhibition clique were, however, too much for him, they were closely banded for their own personal interests, and as it suited them to have Prince Albert for an originator and inventor, instead of Francis Whishaw, Whishaw was systematically put down, and it was even a dangerous thing to speak of him' Henry Cole, as is known, ousted Thomas Webster (and possibly some of his associates) from the Council to the Society's loss for although Webster remained in membership until his death he appears not to have taken office again. Cole's behaviour towards Scott Russell was nothing short of disgraceful and, although there was cause to criticise Bennet Woodcroft regarding the so-called 'Patent Museum', Cole's venomous attack on him before the 1864 House of Commons Special Committee on the Patent Office Library and Museum was totally uncalled for. As the above extracts from the *Civil Engineers and Architects' Journal* intimate, Whishaw was to have been the first Curator of the 'Patent Museum'; perhaps his heart gave out just in time for no doubt his life would have been made miserable by Big Brother Cole of South Kensington who was torment enough for Woodcroft in that regard.

[6] Approximately 260 recruits in the four years 1842–5 (principally in the last three) probably resulted in Society membership being increased by at least a third. In the decade starting in 1842 membership doubled and by the 1870s total membership was about four times the 1840 figure. For the next seventy years membership remained around the 1870s level until a mid-twentieth century leap. 1842 marked a vital watershed in the Society's affairs. The present author is indebted to Dr. R.T. Smith for providing a list of members elected over the 1842–5 period with their proposers. It includes many engineers and several patent agents. During the years in which Whishaw was Secretary members elected were in 1843–104; 1844–51; 1845–66. On resigning the Secretaryship Whishaw, as a Life Member, was in a position to propose people for membership directly. Some of the more noteworthy recruits from a Society viewpoint involving Webster, Bethell and associates were as follows: The fifty-three members proposed by Thomas Webster included Henry Bessemer (steel producer, inventor, Albert Medallist 1872), William Carpmael (engineer, patent agent, whose family connections with the Society went beyond the nineteenth century), William Fothergill Cooke (pioneer of electric telegraphy, Albert Medallist 1867, and with whom Whishaw was particularly closely associated), John Scott Russell (marine engineer who was to follow Whishaw as Secretary to the Society), Joseph Whitworth (pioneer of standardisation in engineering, devisor and provider of 'Whitworth Scholarships', Albert Medallist 1868), Bennet Woodcroft (engineer, founder of a Manchester-based patent agency, first head of the Patent Office), Benjamin Fothergill (engineer, later to be Curator of the 'Patent Museum'). John Bethell's thirty-nine recruits included his brother Richard (later Lord Chancellor Westbury), William Cubitt (engineer and builder, brother and business partner of Thomas who was to be heavily involved in preparatory work for the 1851 Exhibition), William Newton and William Newton Jnr. (engineers and patent agents), Richard Prosser (engineer, inventor, patent reformer who as a member of the Society's 1849–51 patent committee proposed a definition of 'invention' which formed the basis of such definitions in Patents Acts for more than a century), Robert Stephenson (railway engineer, soon to be very deeply involved in the 1851 Exhibition). Charles Holtzapfel's fifteen proposals included William Fairbairn (engineer, patent reformer, Commissioner for the 1851 and 1862 Exhibitions). George Bailey introduced, among others, George Bodmer (engineer and prolific inventor) and

Francis Fuller (a tireless worker in the preparations leading to the 1851 Exhibition). Three noteworthy recruits whose membership fell outside the 1842–5 period were Henry Cole in 1846 (Edward Speer), Charles Dickens, 1849 (William Tooke) and William Siemens, 1849 (Thomas Webster).

[7] Wood, *History, op.cit.,* pp.403–5; Morrell and Thackray, *op.cit.,* p.264, 'The apotheosis of these [British] Association-pioneered exhibitions [in places like Newcastle, Birmingham, Glasgow and Manchester] occurred in 1851, with the "Great Exhibition" at the Crystal Palace in London'.

Appendices

I

Expenses of taking out a Patent in 1814/15

Patent No. 3887, dated 28th of February, 1815, for 'Improvements in the Construction of Locomotive Engines' granted in the names of Ralph Dodds and George Stephenson took rather less than four months to obtain and appears to have been seen through its application stages by someone acquainted with the correct procedures.

The list of expenses following is taken from a document in the possession of the Institution of Mechanical Engineers and is reproduced here by kind permission of that Institution.

Bill for Messrs. Dodds' & Stephenson's Patent 1814, Nov^{r}.

	£	s	d
Attending Messrs. Dodds & Stephenson, taking Instructions for obtaining a Patent for their improvements in the construction of Locomotive Engines		13	4
Drawing Petition to his Majesty for the Patent and fair copy drawing & engrossing		10	0
Affidavit in support of Petition		10	0
Paid Duty and Oath		4	8
Writing to Agent with Petition and Affidavit and instruc^{s}. to enter a Caveat		3	6
Paid Postage of same to London		3	0
Agent attending at the Patent Office to enter a Caveat		6	8
Paid [Agent for above service]		10	6
Attending at the Attorney and Solicitors General's Office for the like purpose		6	8

	£	s	d
Paid of each		10	0
A further description of the Invention having been required at the Attorney General's Office. Agent attending Mr. Richards thereon and writing me		6	8
Writing Mr. Dodds for the necessary information in order to compleat Caveat and clerk's Journey to Benton Moor with letter		15	0
Horse hire		7	6
Writing Agent with further information		3	6
Postage		2	0
Agent attending at the Attorney General's Office with same and Caveat was completed		6	8
Copy of Petition and Affidavit for Agents		6	0
Paid on leaving Petition at the Secretary of State's Office for an Order of Reference	2	2	6
Paid at the Attorney General's Office for his report	4	4	0
Paid at the Secretary of State's for his Majesty's Warrant for the Bill to be prepared	9	1	0
For a Clerk of the Patents preparing Bill for the Sign Manual	22	19	0
Paid for Sign Manual	9	1	0
Paid fee & Stamps at the Signet Office	7	13	0
Office Keeper		10	6
Gratuity	2	2	0
Paid at the Privy Seal Office	7	8	0
Office Keeper		10	6
Gratuity	2	2	0
Paid for Preparing, Ingrossing and Inrolling the Patent and Stamps, and passing the Great Seal	44	15	0
Agents and Solicitors' Fee Soliciting Patent through the several Offices	15	15	0
Porters and Messengers	1	1	0
Agent attending at the Mail Coach Office with Patent and Paid Booking		7	2
Paid Carriage and Porterage		5	8
Fair Copy of Patent		10	0

	£	s	d
1815, March			
Specification			
Attending you taking Instructions for Specification		6	8
to enroll drawing draft of Specification	1	13	4
Fair copy of same for Perusal		12	6
Writing to Mr. Dodds with same re Clerk's Journey with d°		15	0
Horse hire		7	6
Attending with Mr. Stephenson as to getting the Plan copied for the Specification and attending upon Mr. Th°. Bell and explaining same to him and giving him instructions to Copy same on Stamp to be in readiness ['on stamp to be in readiness' probably represents payment for duty stamp prior to filing of 'Plan']		6	8
Attending Mr. Stephenson Perusing the Plan of draft of Specification when it appeared you had made an improv[t] in the Engine which rendered it necessary to redraw the detail of the Specification		6	8
Redrawing draft detail of Specification	1	6	8
1815, April 5			
Attending Mr. Stephenson this day perusing the Plan and comparing and examining same with draft of Specification and correcting same when it was finally settled		13	4
Ingrossing Specification		16	8
Paid duty and Parchment	5	5	0
Attending upon Mr. Bell with same to make the necessary alteration in the Plan		6	8
Paid Mr. Bell for drawing Plan & altering same	2	2	0
[April] 8: Attending Mess[rs]. Dodds & Stephenson this day reading over and attesting, their executing same & also taking acknowledgement as a Master extra in Chancery		13	4
Copy of Specification for Mr. Stephenson		12	6

	£	s	d
Writing to Agent with the Specification Parcel to the Coach Office and paid		7	2
Paid Carriage and Porterage to London		5	8
Agent attending at the procurement office with Specification		6	8
Several attendances before it could be procured		6	8
June 20: Attending again this day when obtained same		6	8
Paid Inrolling same		2	6
[June] 27: parcel to the Coach Office and paid Booking		3	10
Paid carriage of Porterage of Parcel from London		5	8
Letters and Messengers		10	0
	£158	12	4

Author's Note:
It is somewhat surprising, since no opposition appears to have been entered against this petition, that an Attorney General should at this period have required 'a further description of the invention' (Item 11). It may be that the Attorney General was not unaware that two patents for railway locomotives had fairly recently preceded and were in force. One had been granted only three years before the date of the Dodds/Stephenson application (Blenkinsop, 1811). The other was that of Trevithick, 12 years earlier.
A further interesting feature lies in the specification drawings. These were re-drawn because the inventors had made improvements in the weeks following their application. Therefore the specification drawings included features not disclosed to the Attorney General!

IIA

Official Fees payable on Applications for Patents, 1826

Fees paid when filing specifications (following grant) are not included.

Few Irish patents were sought but as the nineteenth century progressed the desirability of obtaining a Scottish patent in addition to one covering England and Wales became greater.

An Order was made by the House of Commons, for Returns of the Expenses incurred at different Public Offices in taking out Patents (in England, Scotland, and Ireland) independent of the Specification; 23 March, 1826.

	£	s	d
1. *Return from the Office of the Secretary of State for the Home Department, England*:			
Reference to the Attorney or Solicitor General	2	2	6
Royal Warrant	7	13	6
With an addition of £1 7s 6d if the patent of invention extends to His Majesty's colonies and plantations abroad; and if the patent is granted to more than one person, an additional fee upon the Royal Warrant of £1 7s 6d for each additional person.			
King's Bill	7	13	6
With an addition of £1 7s 6d if the patent extends to the colonies; and if granted to more than one person, an additional fee upon the King's Bill of £1 7s 6d for each additional person.			

	£	s	d
2. *From the Office of the Secretary of State for the Home Department, Scotland:*			
Reference to the Lord Advocate	2	2	6
Royal Warrant and Stamp	16	7	0
And if granted to more than one person, an additional fee of £2 15s for each additional person.			

	£	s	d
3. *From the Office of the Secretary of State for the Home Department, Ireland:*			
Reference to the Lord Lieutenant	2	2	6
Warrant and Stamp	9	3	6
And if granted to more than one person, an additional fee of £1 7s 6d for each additional person.			

Whitehall, 6 April 1826

Signed by
Geo. R. Dawson

	£	s	d
4. *Return from the Attorney or Solicitor General's Offices of the expenses incurred there for* taking out a *Patent for England:*			
To the Attorney General for his Report	3	3	–
To the Clerk	1	1	–
If a Caveat be entered, the Clerk receives		5	–
To the Attorney General, for his approving, settling, and signing the Bill	5	–	–
If the Patent is opposed (which sometimes happens) the following Fees are charged:			
To the Clerk for every Summons, summoning the parties to attend before the Attorney General	5	–	–
To the Attorney General, for the hearing of the parties, by themselves, or their agents and witnesses; each party	2	12	6
To the Clerk		12	6

The same Fees are paid, whether the patent passes the office of the Attorney or the Solicitor General.

10 April 1826 Signed by

H. Haines and *H. Owens*

Clerks to the Attorney and Solicitor General.

5. *Return from the Patent Office of the Attorney General, of the expenses incurred there for taking out a Patent for England:*

	£	s	d
Stamp Duty on the Warrant from the King to prepare a Bill for his Majesty's signature to pass the Great Seal	1	10	–
To the Clerk of the Patents for preparing the Bill and Docquet, and his fee	5	10	6
Stamp Duty on the Bill	1	10	–
Ingrossing Clerk	1	1	–
To the Clerk of the Patents, for preparing and ingrossing two Transcripts of the Bill to be passed through the Signet and Privy Seal Offices, parchment for such Transcripts, and transmitting the same to those offices; each Transcript 13s 9d	1	7	6
Stamp Duty on each Transcript, £1 10s	3	–	–

10 April 1826 Signed by

M. Poole, Clerk in the Patent Office.

6. *Return from the Signet Office of the Fees payable there for a common Patent for an Invention, for England; and also for Ireland:*

For England £4 7s For Ireland 3 3 –

Signet Office,
10 April 1826

(signed) *Tho*[s] *Venables*,
Deputy Clerk of the
Signet attending.

7. *Return from the Privy Seal Office, of the ordinary expenses payable there, for a grant of a Patent for an Invention passing the Privy Seal for England:*

	£	s	d
Office Fees	4	–	–
Stamps		2	–
	4	2	–

Privy Seal Office
April 1826

John Thomas Fane,
Clerk of the Privy Seal in attendance.

8. *Return from the Lord Chancellor's Patent Office, of the Fees payable there on a Patent for an Invention for England, passing under the Great Seal:*

	£	s	d
Patent Office	5	17	8
Stamps	30	2	0
Boxes		9	6
Deputy	2	2	0
Hanaper	7	13	6
Deputy		10	6
Recepi	1	11	6
Sealers		10	6
	48	17	2

Every additional name pays an additional fee to the Hanaper of £2 12s 6d

Patent Office, Adelphi
17 April 1826

(signed) *James Selon,*
D.C. Patents

IIB

Exactments at Repositories of Patent Records

Following grant a patent had to be enrolled at one of three offices holding state records, to be followed within a period specified at grant (usually two to three months) by a specification. Fees were payable at grant and specification enrolment stages but the patentee may already have expended several small amounts (often not small in total) at these offices before petitioning for a patent.

It was wise practice to ascertain whether a patent had been granted for an invention of similar subject-matter to that of the would-be patentee before embarking on the expense involved in filing an application. For this records had to be searched in any or all of the three offices of record where the filing systems consisted at best of alphabetical indexes only, of little use when carrying out what was usually a purely subject-matter search. Although the fees and other charges tabulated below appear small, the actions to which they relate usually had to be repeated many times and expenses could mount up accordingly.

The charges in lists below are taken from An Essay on the Law of Patents for New Inventions by John Dyer Collier, 1803. The author of this work was clearly well pleased with what he regarded as a highly satisfactory system and extracts from his chapter entitled 'Repositories of Patent Records' (more especially from pages 195–200) are given in order to provide an insight into pre-1852 practices as much as to provide an indication of charges. It merits mention that it was forbidden for an enquirer to make his own copy if he were fortunate enough to find useful information in any of the documents called for.

Patents for new inventions are enrolled in the Court of Chancery. They are under the direction of the Master of the Rolls, who is the chief clerk; in his custody are such enrolments and treaties as are not of high antiquity.

The repositories of the Court, with which the patentee is principally concerned, are those distinguished under the names of the Chapel of the Rolls, the Petty Bag Office, and the Six Clerks' Office.

In the Rolls Chapel the different classes of records are eighteen in number. The patent records begin with a small roll of Edward V and are continued down to the present reign. Upon these are enrolled all patents for creations of honour, grants of charters of incorporations and liberties, grants of offices, denizations, patents for new inventions, etc.

These rolls are annually made up by the person appointed in rotation for the Riding Six Clerk, from the Privy Seals, or signed bills; from which also the patents and other instruments are engrossed, in order to be passed under the Great Seal by the several officers concerned. As soon as these enrolments are made, they are delivered by the Riding Six Clerk into the Petty Bag Office, in order to be examined by the senior clerk of the office, by whom the patent rolls, and the privy seals or signed bills are remitted into the Rolls Chapel.

The following are some of the fees payable at this office:

	s	d
For search of the calendar each year, under each name	1	–
For taking down every roll	2	6
For taking out any instrument out of any bundle	6	8
For each sheet copied (close)	5	6
For certificate of being a true copy	2	–

In the Petty Bag Office are sixteen distinctions of public records, among which are enrolments of specifications of patent inventions from the 8th of Queen Anne to the present time. These are put up with the surrender of offices during the same period, into seventy-three bundles, and are entered in a calendar, with an alphabetical index referring to each bundle. The persons who have the custody and arrangement of the records in this office are the three clerks of the Petty Bag, who jointly appoint an assistant, whose duty it is to arrange, take care of, and attend with the records when legally required during the office hours, from ten o'clock to two o'clock, and from five o'clock to eight o'clock in the evening, every day, holidays excepted. The clerks receive no remuneration for this duty excepting the appointed fees.

The following are some of the fees:

	s	d
Searching for a specification any number of years, and inspecting the same	1	–
Copying per folio, of seventy-two words, besides stamps	8	–

There are complete and correct alphabetical calendars or indexes to each distinction of records under the care of the Six Clerks, whereby any record may be immediately referred to. The records in this office are sorted, bundled, and entered into a calendar at stated periods. Certain fees of the Six Clerks' Office:

	s	d
Search of every record transmitted into the Record Office	1	–
Copies of records in dormant cases, per sheet		8
Attendance on persons desiring the perusal of any record	6	8

The Rolls Chapel is in Chancery-lane, and appears fit to receive the records; they are of easy access, and are placed in presses somewhat removed from the walls. The records of the Petty Bag Office are in the Rolls yard; the building is detached from the surrounding houses, and is deemed sufficiently substantial, and well adapted to the purpose to which it is applied. The splendid edifice of the Six Clerks Office stands on a portion of the ancient garden ground of Lincoln's Inn.

III

The Patent
by
'The Author of the Graces, 1776'

Happy the man who duly pays his debts,
He still more happy, who a Patent gets,
This prose enlivens, and adorns the rhime,
Lifts the low thought, and stamps it with sublime;
Catches the eye, allures that erring sense
Ere steady judgment can her reign commence,
Like copper plates at which men–children look,
And praise the prints before they read the book.

Hail to the Patent! Which enables man
To vend a folio–or a warming-pan.
This makes the windlass work with double force,
And smoke jacks whirl more rapid in their course;
Confers a sanction on the doctor's pill,
Oft' known to cure, but oft'ner known to kill,
What man would scruple to resign his breath,
Provided he could die a patent death!

Hail to the Patent! That at Irwin's shop
Improves the flavour of a currant-drop.
This gives to washes charms unknown before,
By vestals practis'd, practis'd by the whore,
Nor less by those, who tastefully aspire,
And look like ladies drest in men's attire.

This too can make an engine squirt so high,
As to o'er flow the parlour next the sky,
That he who sleeps, shall wake and start amain,
And think the gen'ral deluge come again;
Impart a property to all machines,
To Milk of Roses, and to magazines;
To folly's features give the face of sense,
And raise a trifle into consequence,
Whate'er it be, a pinchbeck or a toy,
A Tyburn caxon or a dalmahoy.

So Puff's engaging art ('tis all in all)
Can sink the great, and magnify the small;
Silver to tin, or tin to silver turn,
And of a Jordan make a Roman urn:
Alike from all things he derives applause,
An English pipkin, or a Tuscan vase;
On modern pictures stamps an ancient name,
And robs the dead to give the living frame.

The time may come when nothing will succeed,
But what a previous Patent hath decreed;
And we must open, on same future day,
The door of Nature, with a patent key.

My very wig, tho' somewhat worse for wear,
Is patent-made, and leke of patent hair;
Nay e'en my shoe a vast importance takes,
Gloss'd with the genuine Patent Blacking Cakes,
Those cakes, of which the author well may boast,
That shine so brightly–in the Morning Post.

Patent-ribb'd stockings too my legs invest,
For what's a leg, unless 'tis patent-drest?
Since Patents are obtain'd as fancy wills,
For jacks, and wigs, and Justly-Famous Pills
Ought not the bard this instrument to gain,
That, as he sows, he too may reap the grain?
Vain thought, and vainer the attempt! For he
Who keeps the seal, will not remit the fee.

But why on Patents of this nature dwell?
Would not a Patent–place do full as well?
No matter whether I've a head or not;
Where int'rest rules, the parts are quite forgot.

For instance now–observe the Board of Trade,
And See what Lords Commissioners are made!
Would not a stranger think they really knew
Commerce in theory and in practice too,
Knew all its channels, various as they spread,
And trac'd their sources to the fountain-head?
Of trade, alas! Abroad, or trade at home,
Pray what knows Bamber or poetic Soame?
Gascoigne in Chanc'ry hath been known to sit,
And Jenyns long has figured as a wit,
But never shown it with so good a grace
As now–I mean, by keeping in his place.

Patents all the Rage

The lines following were sung at the Covent Garden Theatre in 1798, probably during an interval between scenes of a comedy. The third and fourth lines of the first verse were repeated as a chorus following that and ensuing verses. (The present author is indebted to Brian Caswell of the Patent Office for drawing these lines to his attention.)

In every clime and at every time some fashions have had sway,
And curious strange and simple things by turns have had their day,
No wonder then in this great Town in such a polished age, Sir,
When art and genius are combined that patents are the rage, Sir.

Our clothes, our physic and our food, with many queer utensils,
Must all be marked with Patent Stamps like warming Pans and Pencils,
In mentioning the various Arts you'll think I'm ringing changes,
We've Jacks and Grates and Kitchens too, and also Kitchen ranges.

We have patent fleecy hosiery will open every pore,
And such ills as Gout and Rheumatism soon kick you out of door,
We've also Pills to kill or cure, Perfumes to please your Noses,
With Lozenges, and currant drops, and Warren's Milk of Roses.

In Paternoster Row, we have a Patent Book of Knowledge,
What pity 'tis not infused among our Blades at College,
Then by Patent they could preach or pray, and wisdom
ne'er lacking,
Would shine like Boots and Shoes well blacked with Baily's Patent Blacking.

We've a Patent Urn and a Patent Churn, with Candlesticks and
 Snuffers,
But some are rude enough to call inventors only puffers,
Tho' in execution Week now to prevent domestic wrangle,
The Men may get the washing up with patent Mill and Mangle.

Was Phaeton now with the Sun to run his course again Sir,
With patent Harness, Wheels and whip, divinely made by
 men, Sir,
His day's work He with ease may do guide the Sun safe to
 Bed, Sir,
And light the world with patent Lamps, to shine forth in its
 stead, Sir.

Lord Chesterfield said to his Son, mind grace in all you do Sir,
Even paring of your pretty nails, or buckling of your Shoe Sir,
And when seated on a private seat, there leaving a deposit,
That Business you may do with grace, in a patent Water Closet.

Then we have got true Patent shot, with Gun powder and Gigs
 Sir,
We've patent Cauls and patent Hair and Ladies patent Wigs
 Sir,
There's patent paste will lather in haste, Razors to please all
 faces,
But most pleasing of these pleasing things, are pretty patent
 places.

We've Medicines by Patent, in every Street now sold Sir,
Which if you'd take you'd live as long as the Patriarchs of old,
 Sir,
But enemies to Physic at such blessings will be scoffing,
And die just to enjoy the sweets of a good snug patent Coffin.

IV

A Notice regarding a Society of Arts' Award Winner and his patented Invention

Notice inserted by the Society of Arts in 1798 in The Gentleman's Magazine *(Vol.LXXXIII; pp.97) regarding one of the Society's award-winners who later took out a patent. (The notice included a wood-cut not reproduced.)*

MR. ADAM SCOTT'S MOLE-PLOUGH

The Society for the Encouragement of Arts, Manufactures, and Commerce, in the year 1797, previous to the date of any Patent for such an Instrument, gave a Bounty of Thirty Guineas to Mr. ADAM SCOTT, of Guildford, in Surrey, for his invention of a Machine for the purpose of under-draining Land, called by him a MOLE-PLOUGH, which plough is reserved in the repository of the Society for the inspection and use of the Public and a Print and Description thereof has been published in the Fifteenth Volume of the Society's Transactions; and, in the opinion of experienced workmen, such Ploughs can be made and sold in London at the price of Two Guineas and a Half each.

The Society, therefore, in order to prevent any imposition on the Public, by being compelled to purchase such Ploughs at the enormous price of Ten guineas, under the idea of a Patent having been obtained for the sole making and vending them, think proper hereby to state, that any person is at liberty to inspect Mr. SCOTT'S Plough, and take a Drawing or Model of it, for the purpose of making them, by applying to the proper Officer, at the Society's House, any day, Sundays and Wednesdays excepted, between the hours of ten and two.

This notice was repeated in the Society's Transactions *(Vol.VI (1798), pp.xiv–xvii) concluding with a statement of the Society's aims:*

> A circumstance has occurred during the last Session, which it is necessary the Public in general, and more particularly all those who may intend to become Candidates for the Society's Rewards, should attend to; it is this:-
>
> In the year 1797 a Bounty of Thirty Guineas was given to Mr. Adam Scott (see Vol.XV.) page 226), for his invention of an Instrument, called by him a Mole-Plough, on condition of the Plough being left with the Society for the use of the Public and it was stated, that these Ploughs could be sold in London at the price of Two guineas and a half each. Many months had not elapsed, before an Instrument, very similar in its construction to that of Mr. Scott, was offered for sale at the enormous price of Ten Guineas, under the idea of a Patent having been granted for the sole making and vending such Instrument; and it appeared, by a letter received from Mr. Scott, that he had himself acted as an agent in the sale thereof. This induced the Society to resolve, that Mr. Scott cannot, henceforward, be admitted a claimant for any reward from them.
>
> There remains now only again to repeat, that the ingenious, of both sexes, are invited to submit their works and their inventions to the inspection of the Society, from whom they will receive every attention and encouragement their merit may entitle them to, and thereby secure to themselves not only honour and profit, in the present instance, but have also the pleasing consciousness that their names will stand recorded to posterity, among those who have contributed to the increase of the Arts, the Manufactures, and the Commerce of their Country; from whence alone the interest, the riches, and the substantial and permanent glory of the Kingdom, can arise.

V

Newspaper advertisement of 1814 regarding a patented article purporting to have the approval of the Society of Arts

Society for the Encouragement etc., London, Dec. 21 1814

The Public are respectfully informed, that Mr. George Stratton of 185, Piccadilly, having advertised what he terms A PATENT STEAM KITCHEN RANGE, in a way calculated to induce the Public to believe that his Steam Kitchen Range has had the sanction of this Society, I am directed to state, that no approbation from them has been obtained by Mr. Stratton; and, further, that the Society from the general principles they profess, do not patronise articles for which patents have been obtained; and I am further directed to annex the following Resolution, dated March 18, 1813 – 'Resolved, It appears to this Committee (Mechanics) that after a very particular and full examination of the several Ranges and apparatus for cooking, made by different Persons, the committee are of opinion, that Mr. Stratton's has not sufficient claims to novelty or general usefulness over others now in use so as to enable the Committee to recommend Mr. Stratton's to a preference' - This Resolution was confirmed by the Society on the 14th of March, 1813.

By nom, *Charles Taylor*, M.D.Sec.

VI

Some Patentee Recipients of Society of Arts' Awards and Some Patentee-Members of the Society

Material extracted from information researched by D.G.C. Allan, formerly Curator/Historian of the Society

During the years 1755–99 some forty of the Society's award winners also received patent grants. Most of the subjects involved fell within the purview of the Society's Committee of Mechanics and related patent grants showed an increase in the later years of the period covered. This was in line with the general rise in grants during the final years of the eighteenth century, e.g. 643 patents are recorded for the decade 1790–99 compared with 296 for 1770–79. The cases falling within the Society's 'Chemistry' classification did not follow the same pattern, they were too few to illustrate a trend. While troublesome to the Society and no doubt frustrating to its paying members, if there were only forty award winners in forty five years who failed to abide by the rules, then the Society would seem to have been effective in impressing its conditions on applicants and indicating its displeasure when award winners erred.

Members of the Society who took out patents were more numerous. Sixty-eight in the single year 1794 are set out below from a list compiled by Dr. Allan. Although the sixty-eight patentee members may seem few, from a Society viewpoint they should be seen against a paying membership at the time in the region of six hundred. As background to the patent situation in 1794, the total number of grants that year was fifty-four and the total number of patents in force approximately seven hundred and fifty.

Not surprisingly few names and fewer of the subjects listed are of obvious significance today. Patents for candle sticks, carriage wheels, churns, curing smoky chimneys, horse shoe nails, ploughs and seed drills may nevertheless indicate meritorious improvements on life in another age. As with patents of any period, some of the inventions may have had little merit while some apparent failures may have provided stepping-stones for later innovators. The small number of names recognised by the present writer are set out after the list, with some reasons why they appear significant to him.

Patentee-members of the Society in 1794

1. ASHTON, Isaac	1793	Weight resistance
2. BANCROFT, Edward	1775	Dyeing
3. BARCLAY, Robert	1790	Printing
4. BENTHAM, Samuel	1791	Planing Wood
	1793	Fire irons
	1793	Working wood
	1795	Facilitating manufacting processes
	1811	Constructing wharfs, piers and bridges
	1812	Underwater masonry
5. BENT, William	1778	Stove grates, ship blocks
6. BOULTON, Matthew	1797	Raising water
7. BRAMAH, Joseph	1778	Water closet
	1783	Water cock
	1784	Lock
	1785	Boiler
	1790	Pump
	1793	Fire-engine
	1794	Increasing power
	1797	Casks
	1798	Locks
8. BRODIE, Alexander	1761	Fire-stoves
	1780	Ship stove
	1786	Iron tires
9. CLAGGETT, Charles	1788	Musical instruments

10. CLARKE, Richard	1783	Kiln
11. CLAY, Henry	1772	Japanned paper
	1778	Japanned buttons
	1786	Dyed buttons
	1790	Buttons
	1792	Carriage panels
	1796	Coal carriage
	1798	Locks-saving water
12. COATES, George	1789	Cleaning linen
	1797	Horse-shoe nails
13. COLLINS, Benjamin Charles	1791	Grate
14. COLLISON, John	1782	Alkali
15. COX, Robert Albion	1768	Smelting
16. CROOK, Thomas	1795	Curing smoking chimneys
17. DAWSON, William	1791	Bobbin lace
18. DESORMEAUX, James Lewis	1790	Dyeing silk
19. DOWNER, Henry	1790	Door spring
20. DRIVER, William	1783	Breaking stones etc.
21. EDWARDS, John	1798	Navigation instruments
22. FORDYCE, George	1774	Sugar-making
23. FROST, Thomas	1781	Stocking-frame
24. FRY, Joseph	1795	Roasting cocoanuts
25. GLENNY, George	1791	Potashes
26. GOODWYN, Henry	1797	Masher for brewing
27. GOWER, Charles	1792	Improving animal oil
28. GREEN, Joseph	1793	Heating rooms
29. HOLLAND, George	1788	Warm clothes
	1790	Warm clothes
	1792	Hosiery
30. HORTON, William	1771	Knitting frame
	1776	Stocking frame
	1778	Network machine
31. JACOB, Joseph	1769	Carriages
	1783	Carriage wheels
32. JEFFERYS, Thomas	1775	Making globes
33. JEFFREYS, George	1791	Dyeing
34. JOHNSON, John	1770	Tanning leather
	1777	Binding
	1779	Fire prevention
	1796	Curing smoking chimneys
35. JOHNSON, William	1788	Overcoming resistance in mechanical operations

36. JONES, Edward	1794	Saddle tree
37. JONES, John	1777	Air pump
38. JONES, Francis	1765	Knitting machines
39. LEWIS, Thomas	1785	Truss
40. MILES, John	1787	Lamps
41. MOORCROFT, William	1796	Horse-shoes
42. NASH, John	1797	Bridges
43. NOUAILLE, Peter	1770	Silk guider
	1774	Silk strings for musical instruments
44. PARKER, Thomas	1792	Mill engine
45. PARKER, William	1781	Support for candlesticks and like devices
46. RASTRICK, John	1777	Barrel churn
47. ROBERTS, Samuel	1790	White metal candlesticks
	1798	Table candlesticks
	1798	Nosles of candlesticks
48. ROBINSON, Thomas	1780	Kitchen range
49. RUSSELL, John	1796	Selenographia (apparatus to exhibit moon features)
50. SHERSON, Robert	1780	Marine metal (one patent)
51. SMITH, Edward	1780	Marine metal (one patent)
52. SKIDMORE, John	1786	Ornamenting stoves,grates, chimney pieces etc.
	1799	Casting iron
53. SMITH, John	1770	Gold and silver buttons etc.
	1783	Printing
54. SMITH, Nathan	1798	Vapour baths
55. STRUTT, Jedediah	1758	Stocking frame
	1759	Stocking frame
	1770	Portable fire stove
56. TAYLOR, William	1765	Knitting machine
	1793	Air furnace
57. TURNER, Thomas	1798	Locks
58. WALKER, John	1776	Spring saddle
59. WARD, John	1779	Stocking frame
60. WEDGWOOD, Josiah	1769	Ornamentation of porcelain
61. WHITE, William	1762	Crucibles
	1789	Ventilation
62. WHITMORE, William	1789	Pump for ships
	1790	Making shanks for buttons
	1791	Mashing grain
	1796	Weighing machine

63. WILKINSON, John	1765	Life belt
	1774	Cannon
	1789	Cannon
	1790	Life saver
	1790	Leadpipe
	1792	Rolling iron
	1794	Cast metal
	1799	Boilers
	1799	White lead
	1808	Cast iron
64. WILSON, George	1792	Postal time marker
65. WILSON, Thomas	1781	Medicine
66. WINLAW, William	1785	Corn Mill
67. WINTER, George	1786	Seed drill
68. WRIGHT, John	1756	Raising steam
	1773	Malleable iron
	1787	Drill plough

Edward Bancroft, described in patent documentation as 'Dr. Edward Bancroft of Downing Street, Westminster, Doctor of Physick', was born in colonial America where he became acquainted with Benjamin Franklin and Joseph Priestley. His patent of 1775 was for a yellow dyestuff from the bark of an American tree and its history provides an example of biters bitten. As the term of his patent grant was nearing its end, Bancroft petitioned to have it extended. The Commons was ready to allow an extension conditional on a maximum stipulated sale price for the dyestuff. Swayed by the arguments of a group of Manchester textile people (always ready to make use of profitable developments without benefit for the devisor), the Lords refused. The patent expired at the end of its normal term and the market price of the dye immediately rose to double the figure the Commons had specified. Bancroft's 'Phylosophy of Permanent Colours' (published 1794 and in expanded form in 1813) became a classic. In it he supported and gave fresh authority to earlier observation on the theory of dyeing which was of immense importance to the future of the industry.

Samuel Bentham – younger brother of Jeremy, the more celebrated political philosopher – was an authority on maritime matters and a competent hydraulics and general engineer.

When placed in charge of naval dockyards he set to work to mechanise the production of pulley blocks. With the assistance of Marc Brunel and Henry Maudsley he developed a system of mass production far ahead of its time. By its use a workforce of 110 skilled men was replaced by 10 unskilled workers – the shape of things to come!

Matthew Boulton is best known in connection with steam engine development as an associate of James Watt. However, before he took Watt under his wing his Soho (Birmingham) works was known throughout Europe. Employing 1000 men, Soho was on so great a scale as to be unique and provided an example to the world. When the time was right for Boulton, Watt's technical genius was geared to Boulton's entrepreneurial skills and a conjunction of prime importance to England's industrial development occurred.

Among a generation that so often appears to judge the 'greatness' of innovation against the 'invention' of sliced bread, then the most outstanding contributions to civilised life to emanate from the eighteenth century may be **Joseph Bramah**'s suction beer pump and water closet. There was more to Bramah than those useful contributions to human welfare. With 18 patents in his name his capacity for innovation is clear. His hydraulic press may have been his most significant invention from an industrial viewpoint as its use became widespread in a variety of ways where forces of several thousands of tons were required, as in the forging of steel. Not less important to technical development was his early position in a line of precision machine-tool makers – tools that for long gave Britain a lead in the manufacture of metal products.

William Dawson receives few, if any, mentions in volumes of general engineering or industrial history. In his own time his application of a configured drum or wheel to knitting frames was contemptuously regarded as no more than an 'obvious' adaptation of a similar element in a barrel organ. A small step indeed but a great move forward in warp knitting where the range of patterns produced was extended to give that industry a useful fillip. The 'Dawson Wheel' was later profitably applied to other and very different machines.

Joseph Fry, whose wife Elizabeth was a noted prison reformer, was of a pioneering cocoa and chocolate manufacturing family. He carried the family firm through changing times into the early nineteenth century. Incidentally, as the industry moved from eighteenth century chocolate drinking to cocoa as a beverage and to eating chocolate in solid form in the nineteenth, Bramah's hydraulic presses were put to use in the extraction of cocoa butter.

John Nash, Regency architect, left his mark most prominently on London and Brighton but wherever and whenever brickwork is covered with plaster or other 'rendering' the influence of Nash is present.

> 'Augustus of Rome was for building renowned
> And of marble he left what of brick he had found;
> But is not our Nash, too, a very great master,
> He finds us all brick and leaves us all plaster.'

Jedediah Strutt's patent for an improvement to stocking frames had expired before he became a member of the Society of Arts at the proposal of Richard Arkwright in 1782. (For practical purposes there was only one patent for his Derby-rib device, that dated 10th January 1759, his 1758 patent having expired for lack of description within the specified time.) This invention not only revolutionised a branch of the hosiery trade but provided the financial means whereby Strutt became Arkwright's most active backer thereby becoming one of the principal creators of Britain's cotton factory system. Indirectly and unintentionally he assisted an even greater development. An apprentice at one of Strutt's cotton spinning mills disappeared from his home area soon after his apprenticeship ended and was not heard of in England for a long time; this was Samuel Slater now regarded as the father of the American cotton industry.

When **Josiah Wedgwood** was throwing pottery at the wheel at the age of nine he did so in what was then an obscure region of Staffordshire. Largely due to his efforts, this area had become widely known as 'The Potteries' by the time of his death in 1795. Though not solely but nevertheless in great measure due to the genius of Wedgwood, the size and scope of the English pottery industry had been transformed, and Staffordshire had gained a world market with an industry previously dominated by other countries. It is unlikely that this could have been achieved if Staffordshire products had had to travel by pony train from the heart of England to seaports or centres of home consumption. It was Wedgwood who grasped the importance of the success of the Bridgewater canal and led a tough political battle to get a waterway network started to link the Trent and Mersey and begin a new and important form of transport for the varied industries of the Midlands.

William White's name is recognised solely in a Society context. In March, 1761 a premium was awarded to William White for crucibles, then on 25th January, 1762 a patent in respect of 'crucibles of British materials' was granted to 'William White, Potter, of Fulham, Middlesex'. So White was an early, perhaps the earliest, Society award winner to take out a patent after receiving the Society's favour. His second patent for a 'machine for expelling foul air from mines, ships, jails, hospitals, chambers or other close places' is remarkably reminiscent of Dr. Stephen Hales's device of nearly fifty years earlier. Although not in the same category as the other people here described, it can at least be said that Mr. White was a man of enterprise.

John Wilkinson – close friend of Samuel More, the Society's great eighteenth century Secretary – was a prominent iron-master. There was a period towards the end of that century when the output of Wilkinson's furnaces exceeded that of any other iron–master. He was also prolific in useful innovations. His cannon boring device provided the British armed forces with weapons capable of more accurate employment than those possessed by rivals. Adapted for steam engine cylinders, the boring device gave Watt a degree of precision for his engines that had previously eluded him and thus accelerated the development of the steam age. Wilkinson is also credited with launching the first iron boat, (The present writer, now based in Yorkshire, cannot forbear to mention that *The Gentleman's Magazine* reported in 1777 that a small iron pleasure craft had been launched on the Yorkshire Foss on 20th May of that year–a decade before Wilkinson's barge) and of solving the problem of making seamless metal tubes, objects of great importance to nineteenth century engineering. Among his exported iron-work were pipes for the Paris water supply. He was without question, a key figure in giving impetus to the Industrial Revolution.

VII

Rules and Notice relating to Society of Arts' Rewards and Patents

Rules and Orders of the Society of Arts, June 1802 Section XII – Of Rewards

I The chief objects of the attention and encouragement of the Society, in the application of their rewards, are, ingenuity in the several branches of the polite and liberal arts; useful inventions, discoveries, or improvements in agriculture, manufactures, mechanicks, and chemist'y or the laying open any such to the public; and, in general, all such useful inventions, discoveries, or improvements, as may appear to have a tendency to the advantage of trade and commerce.

XIV No person shall receive any premium, or bounty, from the Society, for any matter for which he has obtained or proposes to obtain a patent. Nor shall any model or machine, for which a patent has been obtained, or is proposed to be obtained, be admitted into the repository of the Society.

XV No member who has obtained a patent for any article similar to such as may be produced to the Society shall be allowed to vote either in the committee or Society on that subject.

Transactions, Vol.LIII, 1841, at p.V: General Notice to Candidates, (para. 4)

No person shall receive any premium, bounty, or encouragement, from the Society, for any matter for which he has obtained a premium or reward from any other Society, or for which he has obtained, or purposes to obtain, a patent: it being a condition stipulated with every candidate, that all articles rewarded by the Society shall be freely given up to the public, to be made or manufactured by any person whomsoever.

VIII

Crisis and change at the Society of Arts – 1841–5 Extracts from contemporary Minutes and Transactions

Nov. 3rd 1841: Reports from the Committee of Accounts on the audit were agreed to.

On reading that part of the Minutes which relates to the Vice-President in the Chair having given an Order that the Trustees sell out the sum of £168/10/1 3% Consuls in order to liquidate the bills, salaries and other incidental expenses during the vacation – A Motion was made by Mr. Higgins that it is the opinion of this meeting that the substitution of an Order from the Chair for the confirming of a Motion for the selling out stock from the Society's funds was contrary to *Rules and Orders* – Agreed to.

A Motion was made by Mr. Higgins that it be referred to the Committee of Accounts 'to examine and report to the Society the general state of the Society's funds and resources, the average income and expenditure of the Society for the last three years, their opinion of the financial prospect of the Society, and such other information as they may consider to be connected with this reference' – Agreed to.

Nov. 17th 1841: Wm. Tooke, Esq. V.P. in the Chair. A Report from the Committee of Accounts on reference of Nov. 3rd ... the only remaining resource in the funds is £400 being the balance of the life fund. The Committee further recommended to the Society that the following gentlemen be a Committee appointed to take into consideration the original objects of the Society, the manner in which these may have been interfered

with by more recent Societies, the field which is now open for its labours and the means by which the Society can be rendered more efficient both as regard its objects, management and constitution, and to report generally on the means of increasing its usefulness, and on the course which they would recommend to be adopted; *viz.* – Messrs. Webster & ors.
The Report of the Committee was agreed to.

Nov. 24th 1841: A Motion was made that the Select Committee be requested to make a Report on, or before the 15th of December – Agreed to.
Dec. 1st 1841: This meeting stood as a General Meeting but there not being sufficient Members present the same could not take place.
Dec. 15th 1841: The Report from the Select Committee read, including 'Your Committee are of opinion that while the original objects of the Society should be preserved as strictly as possible and while the poor inventor should ever be considered as having special claims on the notice and encouragement and assistance of the Society, the exclusion of communications connected with inventions for which patents have been obtained and the strictness of the rule respecting communications previously published or rewarded by other Societies has been extremely detrimental to the interests of the Society.'
March 2nd 1842: The Following proposition which had been delivered to the Secretary and which had been hung up the usual time was moved and seconded, *viz*: 'that Art$^{l.}$ 11, Sect$^{n.}$ 12

> "Every person who shall receive any premium or bounty from the Society, shall relinquish all pretensions to a patent for any matter for which he has obtained such premium or bounty", be rescinded.' – Agreed to.

Transactions, Vol.LV (1845), Preface, p.XIV.
Since the commencement of the present session 1841–42, the expediency of increasing the interest of the meetings by the adoption of measures which shall in no way interfere with the original objects of the Society is a question which has occupied the serious attention of the members. Accordingly, it is now the practice of the Society to receive communications on any

subjects of novelty and interest connected with the arts and manufactures of the country, including patent inventions to be read or explained with models and drawings at the Wednesday evening meetings.

The most liberal construction of the intentions of the founders of the Society is, that ingenious industry should be encouraged by every available means, and it is now considered certain that these intentions are but half fulfilled if the poor inventor be debarred the advantage of a reference to the Museum and Transactions of the Society, as the sources of information upon all, or, at least, the most important useful inventions; and it is equally certain that if he trusts to them as a safe reference, while they do not include patented inventions, he takes the risk of wasting his time by inventing again that which has been invented before, as it is notorious that the most important inventions of the present day are secured by patent. It is equally notorious that patents are every day obtained for inventions which prove to be altogether futile.

The patentee who receives a vote of thanks from the Society must not consider that the measure of approbation thus expressed by the Society in publishing his communication is less than that of other inventions of non-patentees for which medals or pecuniary premiums may have been voted. The whole tendency of these regulations, both as regards the proceedings at the weekly meetings and the publication of patent inventions in the Society's Transactions, is to render the Society more extensively useful and valuable as a national institution.

IX

A Councel's Opinion (1855) on the Society of Arts' Early and Later Attitudes to Patents

PATENTS AND THE SOCIETY OF ARTS

SIR, - As the following paragraph, in the admirable address of the Chairman of Council to the first meeting of the Session, "During a period of our social history, when protection and monopoly were held by our most eminent statesmen and most expert statists to be the very tap-roots of commercial prosperity and manufacturing industry, the Society of Arts discountenanced patents and monopolies of every kind," is calculated to convey a wrong impression, I beg, as an old member of the Society, to request the insertion in the *Journal* of the following statement in reference thereto:-

It was a rule of the Society of Arts, in former days, that any invention the subject of a patent could not receive any pecuniary reward, it being considered that the patent was, or ought to be, the reward selected by the inventor himself, and that the funds of the Society should be applied to the encouragement of those meritorious inventors who were prohibited by the cost of patents from securing to themselves property in the results of their own talent and ingenuity.* The inventions rewarded by the Society of Arts were to be given to, or considered the property of, the public; and it would be a most interesting and instructive inquiry, to ascertain how many of the inventions which, during the last 50 years, may be considered as steps in the onward progress of the arts and manufactures, were the subject of patents, or so dedicated to the public by their authors.

About the year 1840 the Society was in such a state of prostration and inanition, that its winding up and dissolution was actually proposed; this was successfully resisted by various alterations and reforms, which, after six or seven years, brought the Society into a state, the foundation of its present prosperity and usefulness. The admission and exhibition of inventions, though the subject of patents, was a leading instrument in the progress of resuscitation, while the reform of the patent laws has been the subject of many committees and of much public discussion at meetings of the Society of Arts, not with the view of discouraging patents, but of making them useful for the advancement of practical science.

I remain, your truly,
THOMAS WEBSTER

Temple, December 5th, 1855.

* It deserves to be recorded on every occasion, that the Society of Arts spent upwards of £100,000 in pecuniary rewards, in addition to honorary and other premiums, during the 87 years of its existence. – See Report of Select Committee, Dec. 15, 1841.

S of A Jnl., Vol.4 (1855/6), p.41.

X

Prince Albert, the Patent Office, 'Patent Museum' and 'Gallery of Inventors'

Evidence of the Prince's close attention to and personal interest in matters relating to the Patent Office as shown in communications with the Society of Arts and Bennet Woodcroft

Passages below bearing the suffix 'R.A.' are extracts from the Royal Archives, Windsor Castle and are quoted with the gracious permission of Her Majesty The Queen.

The present author is indebted to John Hewish formerly of the British Library for bringing documents held in the Royal Archives to his attention.

Giving evidence before a parliamentary committee in 1864, Bennet Woodcroft spoke of an early meeting with the Prince Consort:

> 'Prior to my appointment, the late Prince Consort was quite aware of my having a collection of books and models. The first interview I was honoured with was at the Prince's own request; he saw some of my models in the Society of Arts, and he desired his secretary to ask me to take them on the following day to Buckingham Palace, that he might there examine them at leisure, and from that time he was exceedingly courteous and condescending on all occasions.'

Immediately on election to the Society of Arts in January 1843 Woodcroft had entered into some aspects of the Society's affairs in a lively manner. Within a matter of weeks he was serving on the Committee of Manufactures and was active in support of the Society's exhibitions of manufactures held first in 1846 and then in two or three years following. He had sought the support of industrialists for these displays and when the 1851 Exhibition was in prospect he received a certificate initialled by the Prince authorising him to sound out opinion on the desirability of the proposal:

> 'Professor Bennet Woodcroft has been authorised by His Royal Highness the Prince Albert, as president of the Society of Arts, Manufactures, and Commerce, to collect opinions and evidence with reference to the expediency of forming a great Exhibition of Industry of all Nations to be held in London in the year 1851, in order that His Royal Highness may bring the results of such enquiry before Her Majesty's Government.
> OSBORNE, August 5th, 1849.'

At the close of 1845 the Society's Secretary wrote to Woodcroft requesting him to send a promised paper on the screw propeller. Much could be written of this 'paper' but its immediate interest is that it gave rise to some Woodcroft models going to the Society. A further communication from the Secretary brought a response dated 4th May 1846: 'It would afford me pleasure to comply with your request and send my models to the next meeting, with a brief account of some of the doings of the screw ships, but ...' Models did eventually arrive, for some time later Woodcroft wrote, 'Will you favour me per return with a list of the models you have of mine, and how long the Society is desirous to have them'. A screw propeller of Woodcroft's devising had performed well in trials on the 'Great Britain', as Woodcroft was pleased to recount in his letter. Having made a study of previous attempts at marine screw propulsion, he appears to have had models of some of them prepared for display. The story of a development of great significance to a maritime power could not fail to have the attention of Prince Albert. By reason of these models, his canvassing support for the Society's industrial exhibitions and his work for the 1851 Exhibition, Woodcroft had come to the notice of the Prince on several occasions prior to his appointment to the Patent Office.

At the time of the above correspondence Woodcroft was resident in the Manchester area but moved to London shortly afterwards as an engineering and patent consultant. Appointment as Professor of Machinery at University College, London soon followed, a position that did him no credit; he was totally unsuited to deliver a lecture and his prime interest at that period was promotion of his marine screw inventions. The appointment was brief but Woodcroft clung to the title. His post at the Patent Office had initially been designated 'Assistant Commissioner of Patents', but this title was dropped by the Commissioners who solved one of their loss of office compensation problems by allowing the Lord Chancellor's 'Clerk of Patents' to remain in office, thus relegating Woodcroft to a secondary position to which he never took kindly.

Woodcroft and a small staff were found 'temporary' accommodation in rooms at 25 Southampton Buildings vacated by some of the Lord Chancellor's staff. These they occupied on 29 December, 1852, the date of a Woodcroft interview with Prince Albert. The following extract of a 'Minute of Conversation with Professor Woodcroft' is dated 'Windsor Castle' 29 December 1852':

> 'Professor Woodcroft lately appointed Assistant Com-missioner of Patents attended at Windsor Castle this day by appointment and had a long interview with the Prince who was desirous of learning from him the nature of his employment and what had led to it. In the course of the conversation Professor Woodcroft entered at considerable detail into the difficulties and losses to which Inventors had long been subjected in consequence of their being no Register of Patents available for reference ... Professor Woodcroft had in his private capacity, devoted many years at great expense of time and trouble to an attempt to remedy this evil, and had prepared an index of all Patents, properly classified and arranged ...
>
> HRH questioned Professor Woodcroft very closely as to his opinion of the probable advantage to be derived from adoption of the Plan hinted at by the Exhibition Commissioners to have a place where models of new inventions might be deposited and preserved; and where lectures might be given on Manufactures and Machinery, and exemplified by the sight at the same time of working Models in operation.
>
> Professor Woodcroft thought the importance of such a plan could not be overestimated.

> HRH was anxious to ascertain how far the proposal of the Commissioners would meet with the favour and support of the Manufacturers. Professor Woodcroft undertook to ascertain this privately (but at the same time as information which HRH was desirous of ascertaining) and to communicate the result.' (RA–VIC/F25/132)

As soon as the Master of the Rolls (the Commissioner of Patents most actively concerned with the day-to-day running of the Patent Office) returned to London from his Christmas vacation, Woodcroft reported his interview with the Prince and on 5 January 1853 wrote to the Prince's secretary, 'His Honour coincides entirely in the views expressed by His Royal Highness as to the great practical advantage that would arise to the country from the establishment of a library of the inventions of all countries, with Indices chronologically arranged, of each class of inventions, and also from the establishment of an institution to contain machines and models.

With a view to aid His Royal Highness in such important national works His Honour will give his most zealous efforts for their establishment. ... I have already enquired from several of my Merchant friends if they would support such an institution under the auspices of His Royal Highness Prince Albert, and have obtained favourable answers from each.' Woodcroft went on to say that he already had a large collection of models and others were promised. 'This collection could be got together by myself, and be kept secret until His Royal Highness thought fit to have it made public'. (RA-VIC/F25/133)

HRH was then treated to another lengthy discourse on patent indexes.

Six days later Woodcroft was at Windsor Castle again and on 21 January reported by letter further progress: Richard Prosser, a Birmingham engineer had promised to lend 'several thousand volumes of purely mechanical works which have taken him almost a life-time to collect'. [Prosser's collection of books along with Woodcroft's personal library provided the nucleus from which the British Library Science Reference and Information Division developed.] Further, Joseph Whitworth and Benjamin Fothergill, leading Manchester engineers, 'promised the most hearty assistance' in supporting the proposals for a Library of mechanical books and a Museum of

Machines and Models 'They would bring the subject before the [Institution of] Mechanical Engineers of which they are members at the annual meeting on Thursday next, which is to be in Birmingham.' (RA-VIC/F25/144)

The Prince's response was immediate:

> 'His Royal Highness would wish these demonstrations of the feelings of the mechanicians of Birmingham and Manchester to be encouraged ... The great desideratum hitherto has been to obtain the support of public opinion for the proposed collection of information on inventions, and it would appear that the feelings of the great engineering Towns are quite in keeping with the idea.' (Letter dated, 'Windsor Castle, 22 January 1853'–RA-IC/F25/145)

Woodcroft was keen 'to show what progress is being made in the formation of a Patent Library of inventions in which His Royal Highness Prince Albert has taken so great an interest' and informed the Prince:

> 'The Master of the Rolls has given me permission to attend the annual meeting of Mechanical Engineers which will be held in Birmingham tomorrow, to which I had been previously invited, in order that I may carry out His Royal Highness' views in regard to the Library and Museum ... I shall proceed to Manchester and Sheffield for the same object, and report the result of my labours as I proceed'. (RA-VIC/F25/149)

In Birmingham on 26 January 1853, less than a month from the date on which Woodcroft's clerks started their duties in Southampton Buildings and Woodcroft attended on the Prince at Windsor, a document was prepared that has been described as 'the foundation charter of the British Library, Science Reference Division'. It began,

> 'His Royal Highness Prince Albert having suggested the great national importance (in connection with the Patent Office) of a Library and Museum containing mechanical and scientific works of every age and people for the use of the public; we the undersigned have formed ourselves into a Committee for carrying out so desirable an object ...'

Robert Stephenson headed the list of signatories, followed by Joseph Whitworth, Benjamin Fothergill and a magnificent roll of great engineering names.

From where broken off above, the 'Mechanicals' document continued with 'and we respectfully solicit the Honorable Commissioners of Patents to provide suitable apartments **adjoining the Patent Office** for the reception and investigation of such books and models'.

Woodcroft knew full well when he prepared this document that the Prince's wish was for the museum of models etc. to be located at South Kensington, and no sooner was the Prince aware of what Woodcroft was about on his tour of northern industrial areas than he caused his displeasure to be communicated to the erring traveller. Woodcroft still played with words and, in fact, was never reconciled to 'his' museum being at South Kensington. His letter to the Prince's personal secretary dated '5th Feby. 1853' follows:

'I cannot express how sorry I feel that any mistake should have been made by me in endeavouring to carry out His Royal Highness Prince Albert's views in regard to a National mechanical and scientific Library and Museum.

I had not time in the note I wrote yesterday to give a detailed account of my proceedings.

The letter of the second of Feb^{ry} which I had the honour to receive from you, whilst in Sheffield containing His Royal Highness' objections to the expression in the Birmingham Memorial reached me in sufficient time to correct any such error being made in the Sheffield Memorial.

I immediately sent a telegraphic message to my friends in Manchester, who had volunteered to meet me in Leeds, not to go there but wait my return to Manchester.

On my arrival in that town, I obtained the consent of the party holding the Memorials, to prevent any other signatures being added until they heard from me again, which was agreed to. I also prevented the insertion in the Manchester Guardian of the copies of the Memorial with the present attached signatures until they heard from me on the subject.

The Memorial of the Mechanical Engineers, which was only a sketch by me suggesting the heads of a Memorial to be prepared by themselves, I can get altered and re-signed.

After the interviews I have had with Gentlemen of all profes-

> sions and callings, on the subject of the proposed great national work, I am happy to say that I have not found a single dissentient from the great value of such an undertaking, nor one who has not expressed a strong desire that the proposal may be carried into speedy execution.
>
> I beg humbly to suggest from the experience I have gained on my tour, of the public wishes on this subject, that although the expression, "adjoining the Patent Office", should be required to be expunged from the Memorials, yet that the expression "in connection with the Patent Office" may be retained, because I believe it will expedite the object His Royal Highness is about to carry into effect.
>
> If His Royal Highness will do me the honour to furnish me with His Commands, I will communicate immediately with the parties I have lately seen, either personally or by telegraph.
>
> Perhaps it will not be considered impertinent in me to state that the present Patent Offices are temporary only, and wholly inadequate for the proposed purposes.' (RA-VIC/F25/154)

The 1851 Exhibition was quickly followed by activity directed to the formation of the cultural complex of South Kensington. One of the committees set up to that end was assigned 'to consider the best mode of aiding in establishing a Museum of Inventions'. Chaired by Lord Granville, this committee included Benjamin Disraeli, Henry Labouchere (sometime President of the Board of Trade), Dr. Lyon Playfair and Bennet Woodcroft. On 9 April 1853, Lord Granville wrote to the Prince:

> 'The Committee for aiding the formation of a Museum of Inventions met this morning.
>
> There appears to be no difficulty about obtaining a good collection of Models, but Professor Woodcroft doubts the Patent Commissioners being willing to let us have their Library. The Committee were of opinion that a Collection of Models would be without vitality if disconnected from a library and the printed specification ...
>
> Since the Meeting I have seen the Master of the Rolls, who appears to be much more ready to assist us than Professor Woodcroft, who I thought was not very cordial with Dr. Playfair ... I will, with Your Royal Highness' sanction, call the Committee together again, and invite the Master of the Rolls to be one of it'. (RA-VIC/F25/159)

It may be that the antipathetic attitude of Woodcroft towards Lyon Playfair (now close to the Prince) stemmed from events when both were in Manchester; Woodcroft was already across with Henry Cole; what he so earnestly desired for his museum would certainly not receive the unanimous support of the Society of Arts which was much interested in the broad plan proposed for the South Kensington complex; in addition, and not least, Woodcroft must have been putting the Prince's patience under great strain.

Five years later Woodcroft was still trying to move things his way, as indicated in a letter from Henry Cole to the Prince's personal Secretary:

> *Science and Art Department*
> *South Kensington, London W*
> *5 day of March 1858*
> My dear General
> A Memorial prepared I have no doubt by Mr. Bennet Woodcroft was presented to the Meeting of the Society of Arts last Wednesday, addressed to the new Lord Chancellor urging him to spend the surplus Patent fees in providing new buildings for the Patent Office which should embrace the Library & Models. It did not say the buildings should be in Chancery Lane, but it left it to be inferred that they ought. Being **general** I signed it and it may be well to see that Lord Chelmsford does not pledge himself to undo what has been done at Kensington, which I have reason to know is what Mr. Woodcroft desires. Having committed himself to adopt our rules and system, he has taken all means to break the rules & to alter the system. Having hitherto failed, he is now trying to get away.
> It is right that HRH should know as much.
> Faithfully yours *Henry Cole* (RA-VIC/F26/52)

Woodcroft achieved a commendable degree of success with another project, but again some of his behaviour relative to it was less than commendable. The Society's *Journal* dated 30 December, 1853 carried a notice headed 'Gallery of Inventors':

> The Council have much pleasure in giving publicity to the following letter, which has been received from His Royal Highness the President:-
> Osborne, December 16th 1853

I am commanded by His Royal Highness Prince Albert, to request that you will bring under the consideration of the Council of the Society of Arts, a suggestion which has been made to His Royal Highness, the adoption of which, it appears to him, may perhaps be desirable.

Among the exhibitions of various kinds which are from time to time promoted by the Society, it seems to His Royal Highness that it might prove useful, and could scarcely fail to be highly interesting, if a series of authentic portraits of distinguished inventors, either in art or science, were collected for exhibition on some future occasion, and historically classified.

The names of most of those who are thus distinguished, are probably familiar to the world, and nothing is needed to remind men of the reputation they have so justly earned, or of their works. Still, even in their case, it would be interesting to present us, as it were, with their very features. But there are others who have done scarcely less for the happiness, comfort, and improvement of their fellow men, who are hardly known even by name to the general public, which is daily profiting by their inventions; and it becomes almost a duty towards them, to endeavour, in this manner, to rescue them from oblivion, and enable them to take place among the benefactors of mankind to which they are fairly entitled.

Great care should, however, be taken in the selection, only to include those whose inventions have had an important and beneficial effect in improving the condition of the people generally, and in advancing science, and in whom, consequently, all should feel an equal interest.

An attempt to form a collection of this description might also prove the means of rescuing from destruction many records that may still exist of bygone men, eminent in science or in art - and if a catalogue were added, containing some short biographical sketch of their lives, it might tend to the further useful result of leading others to study and attempt to emulate the means by which such men acquired their reputation.

I have the honour to be, Sir,
Your most obedient Servant,
C. GREY

The Council soon announced that it had started a collection and receipts of portraits were noticed in the *Journal*. At a meeting to discuss the patent laws on 1st February 1854 portraits of inventors were hung around the lecture room and mentioned as 'the beginning of the collection now being made by the Council'. This collection later found its way to the 'Patent Museum' at South Kensington where something over 400 portraits were gathered. In the *Catalogue of the Gallery of Portraits of Inventors, Discovers, and Introducers of Useful Arts* an introductory passage states, 'The following Collection of Portraits, Medallions, and busts has been made by B. Woodcroft with a view to the formation of a Gallery of Portraits ... (*This undertaking has received the approbation of His Royal Highness the Prince Consort and the Commissioners of Patents.*)' [No mention of the appreciable Society of Arts contribution.] Item 1 in the 1859 Catalogue reads:

'Rev. John Harmer. Born at Chalford Bottom, Gloucestershire. Died in 1798. (Drawing in chalk by J.R. Smith bearing the following inscription:- "This, the original likeness of the late Rev. John Harmer, has by his family been presented to Bennet Woodcroft, towards the formation of a National Gallery of Portraits of Inventors, and is the first gift for that interesting and valuable object - 6th Dec. 1853.")'. It would appear from this date that Woodcroft jumped the gun on the Prince!

XI

Extracts from Evidence of Thomas Webster and Henry Cole before a House of Commons Committee in 1864 relating to events preliminary to the 1852 Act and to the Establishment of a Patent Museum

(From House of Commons Sessional Papers 1864: Special Committee on the Patent Office Library and Museum)

The 1852 Patent Act

Thomas Webster

1463. I believe that you prepared, or had something to do with preparing the three Bills of 1851, and the two Bills of the year 1852, which resulted in the passing of the Patent Law Amendment Act of 1852? Yes, I had. The approach of the Great Exhibition of 1851 led to the question of the Patent Law being fairly taken up, and to a Committee of the Society of Arts being appointed for effecting an improvement of the Patent Law, and giving provisional protection to inventors in the Great Exhibition. Inventors are often very badly of accord with each other. The Committee of the Society of Arts divided, and out of that resulted an association that has been called the "Inventors' Association", which now exists, and which has endeavoured from time to time to bring this matter before the public, or before any Committee of Parliament. The result of the deliberations of that Committee and of the Inventors' Association was the first Bill of my Lord Granville of the

Session of 1851, which I prepared, and also another, on a different plan, for my Lord Brougham. Those two Bills were submitted to a Select Committee of the House of Lords, before which a large body of evidence was taken, and which really contains almost the whole history of the requirements of inventors. Then those two Bills were consolidated by myself into a third Bill as the result of that evidence. In the Session of 1851, the Bill, owing to its being returned so late from the House of Commons, was lost. But in the year 1852 two other Bills were prepared, one by myself for Lord Colchester, the Government having been changed, and also one for Lord Brougham, and the two resulted in the present Act of 1852.

Henry Cole

2343. Have the Society of Arts taken an active part in bringing about the present state of things relating to the Patent Laws and Patent Museum? Yes, a very great share; in fact, I consider that the reform of the Patent Laws is due to the Society of Arts; at a time when public opinion was crude on the subject they took a great deal of trouble. In 1849 they appointed an influential committee, consisting of the Marquis of Northampton, Lord Radnor, and Manufacturers and Patent Agents, Mr. Bennet Woodcroft being on that committee; they published three different reports and circulated a quantity of pamphlets; I hold in my hand one of the tracts, for general circulation, intended to promote the remission of the taxes on invention. This was in the year 1850, and, for the first time, the Society of Arts brought together an account of the stages that it was necessary to go through in getting patents; it related how much Privy Seal, Clerk of Patents, Clerk of the Hanaper, Deputy Clerk of the Hanaper, Pursebearer, Deputy Sealbearer, Chaffwax, Deputy Chaffwax, and all that, had to be paid at every stage. Mr. Charles Dickens wrote a story called "A Poor Man's Tale of a Patent", which I believe, had more to do with the reform of the Patent Laws than anything else.

The Patent Museum

Henry Cole

2308. Can you give the Committee any information respecting the time and the nature of the transactions by which the Patent Museum, which is at present located at South Kensington, was first brought there? The story is not a brief one. After the Exhibition of 1851, a considerable amount of public opinion began to be formed on the necessity of industrial education; memorials were presented from the great towns of England; that from Birmingham representing the character of most of them. The memorial from Birmingham noticed the advantages of the Conservatoire des Arts et Metiers, and the Central School of Arts and Manufactures at Paris.

About the same time that those memorials that I have mentioned came up, the Commissioners of 1851, on their own motion, constituted a Committee consisting of Lord Granville, Mr. Disraeli, Mr. Labouchere, Mr. Cardwell, Sir William Cubitt, Mr. T.F. Gibson, the late Professor Forbes, Dr. Playfair, and Professor Woodcroft, Superintendent of Patent Specifications, to consider the best mode of aiding in the establishment of a museum of inventions of the nature indicated in a previous part of their report. The nature of that report may be gathered from their reference to the Conservatoire des Arts et Metiers in Paris, and other similar institutions in Europe. They also refer to the machinery in motion in the Exhibition of 1851, and to the desire for a museum expressed by inventors. They went on to say: 'It is well known that there are numerous valuable models existing in this country, which it would require little effort to obtain, if suitable accommodation could be provided for their display and useful illustration.' Also, they recommended the desirability of exhibiting machines under scientific superintendence, and of co-operating with the Civil Engineers; and other scientific societies. This Committee pointed out that if such a museum of inventions were established, it would be calculated to confer great benefit upon the interests of science and commerce. 'They are of opinion that, for the purpose of rendering such a museum of the greatest amount of benefit, it should not be confined to a mere collection of machines and models, but should embrace as complete a library as possible of all scientific and other works relating to inventions.' They recommended that it should be international, and that it should be a constantly extending museum of inventions. Just at the same time a patentee of considerable eminence, now dead, Mr. Prosser, brought forward the reform of the Patent Law; and he too pointed out that there should be a museum of inventions, the scope of which he defined thus: 'A museum where natural productions from all parts of the world could be arranged and exhibited, and where agricultural statistics could be filed showing the acreage of land under cultivation, and the nature of the crop.' He went on to say: 'Such a museum partly exists at Edinburgh, and although models are cumbersome and expensive to keep in repair, still it may be done, as is shown at the museum at Rotterdam.' He prepared the heads of an Act of Parliament to promote the progress of invention for the improvement of the agriculture and trade of Great Britain, in which he proposed that the Act should provide, 'That a building shall be provided for the purposes of the Act, for exhibiting specimens of the scientific, mechanical, and agricultural productions of Great Britain and her colonies, and the plantations abroad, and also of all other countries.' I mention these facts to show that the idea which existed about that time, from 1851 to 1856, was for a Museum of Scientific Discovery and Inventions. Mr. Bennet Woodcroft happened to have a few models. He had taken interest in that subject, and the late Professor Cowper had some models of machinery also. Mr. Woodcroft being appointed on this Committee by the Commissioners of 1851, became the most active member of the Committee. Mr. Woodcroft's models then were stowed away in Kensington Palace; the Commissioners of 1851 had themselves a considerable number of models (some of them patented and many of them not) also at Kensington Palace. They removed them from Kensington Palace to Gore House, and then they induced the Government of that day to go to Parliament for a vote to provide for those models as well as various other objects, being an inheritance from the Exhibition of 1851. Parliament voted £15,000 to erect that building, which is popularly known as "The Boilers". That iron museum was erected under the direction of the late Sir William

Cubitt. It had, at that time, no connexion with the Board of Trade, or the Science and Art Department; it was erected purposely to receive the collections given by the exhibitors of 1851, and those patent models, as well as other models, then in charge of the Commissioners of 1851; these matters extended from 1854 to 1856. It was necessary to remove the Science and Art Department out of Marlborough House in order to provide for repairing of that place for the Prince of Wales; and the Marlborough House establishment which had been open for four years, was then moved up to South Kensington, Parliament granting a vote of £10,000 for that particular purpose. The department having got to Kensington, the Commissioners of 1851 thought it good policy to hand over those collections from the Exhibition of 1851 to the charge of the Science and Art department, but they did not hand over those models of Mr. Woodcroft's, which, as he stated (Evidence 622), were in his personal care, and not with the Commissioners of Patents.

XII

A *Times* View on Patents, 1851

The following was reproduced in *The Engineer* in 1862. Patents received considerable newspaper and journal attention through half a century from 1850

When it is said that a privilege of this nature is unjust we suppose that what is meant to be asserted is that the community generally is injured thereby; that invention is by this means retarded in place of being promoted; that, in short, an inventor would be more likely to undertake the labour of discovery, if he knew that he must rely wholly upon his own ingenuity for the protection of his secret, than if he was aware that the law would endeavour to aid him in the maintenance of his peculiar privilege. If this be so we admit at once that the opponents of a patent law are in the right. But what reason have we to believe in the truth of this assertion? What circumstances in support of it are adduced by those who make it? We are not speaking of those persons–rare, indeed, in every sense of the term–who seek for no other reward than the pleasure of discovery, and the contemplation of the benefit it will confer on their fellows. The law is not made for such men, neither does its existence interfere with them or their mode of proceeding. They give their inventions to the world, and have their rewards in the admiration and gratitude of mankind. The law, however, regards those who wish to derive a pecuniary benefit from the result of their labour, inquiry and ingenuity; and we ask what such men would do supposing no law existed by which they could secure a property in that which they had discovered? The answer is obvious; they would endeavour to keep their process a secret, and in those cases in which secrecy is impossible they would have no motive to go through the trouble and expense of discovery. Where secrecy might be possible we should find the new process fenced round by every mystery and mystification which the ingenuity of the discover could devise. Secrecy would be enforced on workmen, as far as possible, by keeping them in ignorance; and when this became no longer feasible the sanction of oaths would be employed to that end. A state of most painful suspicion and restraint would be the condition of everyone who was in possession of an invention, and of all whom he employed. A more mischievous, as well as a more disagreeable condition, can hardly be conceived. The necessary uncertainty of success, after every precaution taken, the suffering and expense attendant upon all such endeavour would prove a heavy counterpoise to all expected benefit from the invention. Thus, under this system of no privilege, a large class of discoveries would be wholly without protection, and the remainder would most imperfectly, and with great labour and expense, guarded against unfair appropriation. On the other hand, putting aside for the moment any consideration of the difficulty attending the means of attaining such an end, let us ask what would be the effect of a promise made by society to every *bona fide* inventor that he should enjoy an exclusive property in his discovery for a limited period? If such exclusive property could be insured, if the right itself could be accurately defined and easily acquired, society would, in so far as depended upon the law, have done its utmost to foster a spirit of discovery, because thereby it would render certain such reward as the invention itself really deserved; and to itself society would not by this means do injury, for although there would be some delay in the full and universal enjoyment of the benefit, whatever it might be, resulting from the invention, yet, upon the whole, ultimately there would be a greater harvest of discovery than would accrue from a system by which no reward was provided for him from whom the benefit came. With common men the common motives to exertion must be relied on, and society, by thus judiciously protecting private interest, would promote the general welfare.

XIII

Some Patent Reform Committees with Society of Arts Members

Society of Arts members served on many committees concerned with improvements to the patent system, several of which were appointed by the Council of the Society. Other national organisations, such as the British Association for the Advancement of Science and the Institution of Civil Engineers, also appointed patent committees on which Society members served. Regional committees to do with patents were at times numerous and, again, in some of these Society members played a part, as did William Fairbairn in Manchester and Richard Prosser in Birmingham. The following selection provides a glimpse of the range of people who allowed their names to go forward as committee members.

1849–52. The first committee of the Society to make a major contribution to patent reform suggested very radical changes. Although the 1852 Act fell short of the wishes of some of its members, the committee's deliberations nevertheless appear to have influenced the form that piece of legislation took. The preamble to the committee's first report set out a list of people consenting to serve:

> The following Noblemen and Gentlemen, MEMBERS OF THE SOCIETY OF ARTS, consented, at the request of the Council, to act as a COMMITTEE for promoting Legislative Recognition of the Rights of Inventors, by means of an easy Registration of them, in accordance with the principles agreed on by the Council of the Society in 1849.

The Marquis of Northampton	Sir John P. Boileau, Bart.
The Earl of Radnor	Sir J.J. Guest, Bart. M.P.

The Right Hon. T. Milner Gibson, M.P.
Henry T. Hope, Esq. M.P.
Samuel M. Peto, Esq. M.P.
Sir James Anderson, Glasgow
George Brace, Esq.
Henry Cole, Esq.
Charles Dickens, Esq.
J.H. Elliott, Esq.
John Farey, Esq. C.E.
P. Le Neve Foster, Esq. M.A.
Charles Fox, Esq. C.E.
Wyndham Harding, Esq. C.E.
Edward Highton, Esq.
Capt. Boscawen Ibbetson, K.R.E.
Owen Jones, Esq.
Herbert Minton, Esq. the Potteries
R.S. Newall, Esq. Gateshead
Dr. Lyon Playfair, F.R.S.
Richard Prosser, Esq. Birmingham
Dr. J. Forbes Royle, F.R.S.
W.W. Rundell, Esq. Falmouth
Archibald Slate, Esq. Woodside, Dudley
J. Jobson Smith, Esq. Sheffield
Professor Edward Solly, F.R.S.
Arthur Symonds, Esq.
Professor Bennet Woodcroft

1856. A Memorial presented to the Commissioners of Patents fairly soon after the 1852 Act had been put into effect and a Patent Office established expressed the Society of Arts' concern that matters were not proceeding as well as had been hoped. At root was lack of finance; although very considerable sums were being paid in patent fees consequent on the surge of applications following the 1852 enactment, only a fraction of this inflow was made available for the Commissioners' purposes. The first of eight points made in this Memorial read as follows: 'The whole revenue derived from fees paid for letters patent should be appropriated to such purposes as will promote the beneficial operation and improvement of the patent system, and encourage and aid the progress of invention.' The Memorial then went on to suggest improvements relating to the Patent Office, including a new building, extension of the Patent Office Library's facilities and better accommodation for them, foreign publications relative to patents to be indexed and classified in similar manner to U.K. specifications, and that a series of models be collected to illustrate the progress of invention.

The preamble to the Memorial read as follows:

> Your Memorialists have lately appointed a Committee to consider and report on the best means to be adopted for placing the Patent Office on a footing of efficiency worthy of the nation.

That such Committee consists of the following gentlemen:

W. Bridge Adams
John George Appold, F.R.S.
W.G. Armstrong, F.R.S.
Francis Bennoch
Samuel Holden Blackwell
J.M. Blashfield
John Braithwaite
Jacob Brett
Joseph Burch
F. Crace Calvert
Dugald Campbell
Robert Lucas Chance
Edwin Clark
Henry Cole, C.B.
Charles Cowan, M.P.
Frank Crossley, M.P.
Thomas De la Rue
Bryan Donkin
William Ewart, M.P.
William Fairbairn, F.R.S.
Benjamin Fothergill
Sir Charles Fox
Dr. J.H. Gilbert
Joseph Glynn, F.R.S.
Prof. Graham, F.R.S.
Peter Graham
Warren S. Hale
Henry Hensman
John Hick
Edward Highton
A.C. Hobbs
S.C. Homersham
A.H. Houldsworth
Edward Humphreys
William Hutt, M.P.
Owen Jones
John Bennet Lawes, F.R.S.
George Lowe, F.R.S.
Sir John Macneill, F.R.S.
Henry Maudslay
Charles May
J.E. McConnell
John Joseph Mechi
Herbert Minton
G.F. Muntz, M.P.
Robert S. Newall
Thomas Page
Sir Joseph Paxton, M.P.
John Penn
Ainger M. Perkins
James Platt
Richard Roberts
Titus Salt
Charles W. Siemens
Lord Stanley, M.P.
Robert Stephenson, M.P. F.R.S.
J.D. Morries Stirling
Colonel Sykes, F.R.S.
J.P. Brown Westhead
Prof. Wheatstone, F.R.S.
Joseph Whitworth
George Fergusson Wilson, F.R.S.
Edward Woods
Matthew Digby Wyatt
T.H. Wyatt

1858–62. A trickle of Memorials similar in many of their objectives to that of the Society in 1856 flowed through the late 1850s into the 1860s from a variety of sources including the Institution of Mechanical Engineers and several well-known engineering works. A small degree of repetition of signatures ran through them; it is tempting to surmise a common initiating element. One dated 25th July, 1862 from 'Engineers, Chemists, and persons who from time to time have obtained Letters Patent' is of especial interest by reason of the Society of Arts connexions of several signatories, including John Scott Russell, C.W. Siemens, F.J. Bramwell, William Carpmael, Charles Fox and Charles Cubitt. The Royal Commission set up in 1863 appears to have stemmed or reduced this flow, only to generate expressions of opinion of a different nature.

1875. During the Chairmanship of Lord Alfred Spencer Churchill (1875–6) the Council of the Society was leaning to the view that, though administrative reform was desirable, legislative reform was not required. Clearly there were many people who did not accept such a view, for a group calling themselves 'The Patent Law Committee, 1875' published a list of proposed amendments for the Patents for Inventions Bill, 1875. With C.W. Siemens as Chairman, this group met in the Council Room of the Institution of Civil Engineers and comprised:

Prof. F.A. Abel, F.R.S.
J. Anderson, LL.D.
W.H. Barlow, F.R.S.
F.J. Bateman, F.R.S.
Major Beaumont, M.P.
J.L. Bell, M.P.
Sir H. Bessemer
W.G. Blackie, Ph.D.
F.J. Bramwell, F.R.S.
C.H. Carbutt
E.C. Cawley, M.P.
D. Chadwick, M.P.
E. Chadwick, C.B.
Latimer Clark
Sir H. Cole, C.B.
E.A. Cowper
T.R. Crampton
J. Crosseley, M.P.
Warren de la Rue, F.R.S., D.C.L. Ph.D.
L.L. Dillwyn, M.P.
Sir G. Elliot, Bart., M.P.
A. Orr Ewing, M.P.
J. Fielden, M.P.
P. Le Neve Foster, M.A.
J.H. Gladstone, Ph.D., F.R.S.
P. Graham
G. Gregory, M.P.
T.E. Harrison
G. Haseltine, LL.D.

T. Hawksley
John Head
John Hick, M.P.
Prof. A.W. Hofmann, F.R.S., LL.D.,Ph.D.
W. Hope, V.C.
J. Howard
S.C. Lister
H.C. Lopes, Q.C., M.P.
T.W. Mellor, M.P.
A.J. Mundella, M.P.
W. Newmarch, F.R.S.
Prof. W. Odling, F.R.S.
P.C. Owen, C.B.
J. Hinde Palmer, Q.C.
A.W. Peel, M.P.
Capt. Bedford Pim, R.N., M.P.
Right Hon. Lyon Playfair, F.R.S., C.B., M.P.
Prof. W. Pole, F.R.S.
F.Ransome
E.J. Reed, C.B., M.P.
S. Remington
Robert Sabine, C.B.
B Samuelson, M.P.
General Scott, C.B.,R.E.
J.N. Shoolbred
Lieut.Col. Strange, B.P.S., F.R.A.S,,F.R.S.
Sir W. Thomson, F.R.S., LL.D.
F.W. Webb
T. Webster, Q.C., M.A., F.R.S.
Fr. L. Weinmann, Ph.D.
Sir Charles Wheatstone, F.R.S., D.C.L., LL.D.
Sir Joseph Whitworth, Bart., F.R.S., LL.D.
Prof. A.W. Williamson,F.R.S., Ph.D., V.P.C.S.
E. Woods

LAMBERT MEARS, M.A., LL.D.,
Honorary Secretary

1879–83. Lord Alfred Churchill's remarks in 1876 suggesting that the Society ought not to press for amendments to patent legislation were overtaken by publication of the Government's patents Bill of 1877, in consequence of which Lord Alfred found himself, as Chairman of Council, presiding over meetings of a Patent Law Committee in 1879. His second term as Chairman of Council completed, Lord Alfred's place on the Committee was taken by Sir Frederick Bramwell, in turn followed by Sir William Siemens. How large committees such as those mentioned above functioned can only be conjectured; a few knowledgeable members with personal interests in the subject under consideration probably dominated proceedings. The 1879 Patent Law Committee may have been typical. Eleven meetings of that committee appear to have been held which were attended as follows:

Sir Frederick Abel	6	F.R. Crampton	1
Sir Frederick Bramwell	9	Sir Douglas Galton	4
Alfred Carpmael	5	Sir William Perkin	4
Lord Alfred Churchill	2	Loftus Perkins	4
Hyde Clarke	1	Sir William Siemens	3
Sir Henry Cole	3		

F. R. Crampton was a railway locomotive engineer; Loftus Perkins was the inventor of a steam carriage for use on public roads; other major attenders receive mention in the main text. Sir John Lubbock attended a meeting in 1883, presumably prior to introducing a Bill for the Society.

XIV

A Proposal that a Proportion of surplus Patent Fees be put at the Disposal of the Society of Arts

The following extract from the Preface of How to Make Money by Patents *(1873) by Charles Barlow, patent agent, was quoted by the Chairman of Council during his opening Address of the 1873-4 Session (*S of A Jnl., *Vol.22, p.3.):*

So again we are happy to see that there is a wide-spread opinion that the surplus funds derived from the fees and stamps paid for Letters Patent should be applied to purposes in harmony with the objects of the Patent Laws. This surplus income (after paying the expenses of the Commissioners' office and compensation pensions) amounts to about £80,000 per annum, and is now paid into the Consolidated Fund, whence it may be drawn out for prosecuting the Ashantee war.

Surely it must be unjust that so large a sum, which is extracted from the bone and sinew of the country, *viz.*, the manufacturers, and from the brains of the nation, *viz.*, inventors, should be handed over to the already swollen Consolidated Fund which now amounts to seventy millions sterling per annum. Much has been done by the Commissioners of Patents to facilitate research and to promote the general interest of the inventing classes, and the formation of a convenient and well-stored reading-room, reflects much credit on them and on their excellent Chief Officer; but they have been cramped in their efforts by the exigencies of the Treasury, which has inexorably forbidden any expenditure beyond what was absolutely necessary for conducting the business of the department, and has grasped and retained funds which never ought to have been applied to any other purpose than that of stimulating and rewarding Inventors, and of encouraging Industrial progress. In all probability, this injustice will soon be remedied. It would be a grateful act, meanwhile, if a part only of these funds, say £20,000 per annum, was placed at the disposal of the Society of Arts, to be employed for purposes in connection with the objects of that Society. The Society of Arts is the only association in the kingdom which avowedly attempts to foster industrial invention, and it certainly is not creditable that its income should only be £7,000 per annum, an amount which, after providing for expenses, leaves very little for rewarding struggling genius or inventive talent. The Society of Arts has done much and done well, but its means have been far too limited, and wholly incommensurate with its objects. Now, if the portion of the patent fund indicated were placed at its disposal, or even only £10,000 per annum, the Society would be enabled to take up that position to which it is entitled as the oldest and almost the only society for promoting the Arts and encouraging manufactures.

It would be an act of gratitude, an acknowledgment of the vast prosperity bestowed on this nation through the agency of Inventors, if Parliament were to make a grant of £20,000 per annum, to be applied through this Society in furtherance of interests which are truly national. Let us hope this may come to pass; and to insure it, let every Inventor, and every man who feels that the welfare of this country depends on her manufactures, urge on his representatives in Parliament the urgency and expediency of the proposition.

A reprint from
The Journal of the Royal Society of Arts –

Some Patent Practitioners Associated with the Society of Arts c.1790–1850

The following article by the present author is reprinted slightly abridged from the Journal of the RSA, July–September 1982. It was originally prepared at the time of the centenary of the Chartered Institute of Patent Agents.

Part (i) Soliciting Patents – Old Style

During the eighteenth century and early years of the nineteenth an assortment of people provided assistance to inventors not in a position to see patent applications through for themselves. Few, if any, of these who offered guidance on patents were involved with them as their principal occupations. This was hardly surprising for the procedures for obtaining a patent were ludicrously time-consuming[1] and, more importantly, the number of patents sought was comparatively small.

Fewer than a hundred invention patents were granted in 1800, but even so the number of patent grants had increased tenfold in half a century. In the next half-century the increase was fivefold to give rather more than 500 patent grants in 1850.[2] Even 500 patents a year does not allow of many people making a living out of consultations on patent matters and the prosecution of patent applications, the formulation of agreements and licences and proceedings for the enforcement of rights.

The prosecution of patent applications including the preparation of specifications is the aspect of practice of immediate interest and procedures before 1850 were very different from todays. To understand the pre-1850 patent system it is necessary to appreciate that two distinct instruments were involved in the grant of letters patent for an invention. By 1800 one of them was an anachronism and the function of the other was not understood. The anachronism was the patent deed itself. The other instrument was less than a century old, had no statutory existence, had first appeared at the whim of a legal functionary acting in an executive capacity and everyone had forgotten the circumstances of its birth, yet the highest courts in the land propounded conflicting decisions about it, usually in chastisement of patentees for not knowing its function better than the lawyers; this was the specification. Under the system operative before 1852 an inventor first obtained a patent and then, within a period of time specified in the patent deed, had to prepare a specification and cause it to be enrolled in an office of state. In the specification the patentee described his invention in the best form of which he was aware and in a manner that distinguished the invention from anything previously known.

Even by the 1820s a few people were making the business of obtaining patents a significant part of their activities. Some of these were London solicitors but the advantage in the business lay with some very interesting people indeed. People so engaged were often referred to as 'patent agents' but their activities have little relation to the practice of patent agency as carried out over the last hundred years. Under the heading of 'Attorneys and Solicitors', the Post Office Directory for 1846 had an entry 'Abbott and Wheatley; Francis George Abbott and Robert Benjamin Wheatley, Rolls Yard–and patent agents'. Elsewhere, Francis George Abbott is described as 'Clerk of the Petty Bag', the office held in 1820 by Francis Abbott, who appears in 'Clark's New Law List' for that year under the heading 'Attorneys'. Another 1846 entry is 'Ray, Blunt and Johnstone, 42 Lothbury' with the addition 'David Graham Johnstone, Clerk of Patents to the Attorney General and Solicitor General, Patent Office, 13 Serle Street'. Under 'Patent and Design Registration Offices' could be found 'Poole and Carpmael, 4 Old Square, Lincoln's Inn', the address of another Patent Office under the jurisdiction of the Attorneys and Solicitors General. One of the earliest collections of law reports of patent cases was published in 1816 by John Davies,[3] who stated in his Preface that he had been 'upwards of thirty years in the office of the Rolls Chapel' and had 'for many years been concerned for inventors in soliciting patents for inventions'.

Francis Abbott, John Davies, David Graham Johnstone and Moses Poole all held positions in offices of state through which patent applications had to pass or in which specifications were enrolled. By the 1820s Francis Abbott and Moses Poole had gathered most of the business to themselves with Moses Poole taking the lion's share.[4] Moses Poole will be mentioned later; enough for the present to say that he inherited his position in the Attorney-General's Patent Office from his father, James, who had held the position from 1776.[5] Interestingly, James Poole was in touch with officers of the Society of Arts in the eighteenth century and Moses Poole's membership of the Society extended over more than twenty years from 1818, that is almost from the date of his taking over from his father in 1817 the clerkship in the Attorney General's Patent Office.

So much for the business of obtaining a patent. In the eighteenth century it was an occasional activity of solicitors; in the first quarter of the nineteenth century most of the business was in the hands of officials whose 'Moonlighting' activities must have bathed them in a pleasantly warm glow. Who then, prepared the specifications? When Moses Poole was asked in 1829 if he drew up specifications, he replied, 'Never, it is too difficult a thing for me to undertake'. He was then asked if drawing up specifications was the business of a particular class of persons. He replied that he was in the habit of recommending his clients to go to Mr. Farey, Professor Millington, Mr. Rotch or Mr. Gill.[6] Francis Abbott said at this time that although agents (that is, people like himself who solicited patents) often drew up specifications, in matters of importance such men as Mr. Farey and Mr. Donkin were employed.[7] Before taking a look at the activities of those valuable members of the Society of Arts, Mr. Donkin, Mr. Farey, Mr. Rotch and others, it will be useful to look at the nature of the specification, an odd document that is best prepared by someone with a sound practical background, say an engineer or a chemist, and once written is subject to analysis and dissection by lawyers, and criticism by judges, as if it were a legal document pure and simple.

Under the pre-1852 patent system an inventor was at risk both of not receiving a patent and of piracy, if he disclosed his invention to a third party before his patent was sealed. A Lord Chancellor is reported to have said that 'if he was applying for a patent he would not communicate the secret to his own brother'.[8] But patents were only granted for new inventions. How were the Law Officers, who advised the Sovereign on the allowability of grants, to assure themselves that the applicant was in possession of an invention? Early in the eighteenth century, Law Officers got around the problem by saying in effect to inventors, 'You can have a patent but when you receive it you must state in writing what your invention is and if you do not do this within the time specified in the patent deed the monopoly granted to you will be void and of no effect. Furthermore, if the invention you describe is not new your patent will be invalid anyway.'[9]

The clause voiding patents unless a specification was enrolled first appeared in patent deeds in 1723 but did not become a regular feature until 1734[10] – only twenty years before the founding of the Society of Arts. There were, however, a few specifications before that time. The first is considered to be that associated with John Nasmith's patent of 1711 for preparing a wash from sugar and molasses.[11] Shortly afterwards, in 1718, James Puckle seems to have killed two birds with one stone because he prepared his 'specification' in such a way that it could also be used as a piece of trade literature.[12] James Puckle was a notary public. In 1696 he advertised himself as of 'the Office of Puckle and Jenkins, Publick Notaries, in Pope's Head Alley, over against the Royal Exchange, London, wherein ... Patents, Constitutions, as all the terms of subscription are fully engrossed.'[13]

Specifications took on a new significance in 1778 when Lord Mansfield set aside the patent for Adams' Oil Cement[14] and defined some essential requirements for specifications. For the Adam brothers and others who had acquired patents and prepared specifications before Lord Mansfield's judgement was handed down,[15] this was changing the rules of the game in mid-play. It was a disaster for those distinguished members of the Society of Arts and builders of its house, the Adam brothers. They had already stretched their resources on the great Adelphi project and the patent litigation that ended so bitterly for them was an added financial burden from which they never recovered.[16]

The specification took on an importance greater than had been expected, but for nearly 70 years after Lord Mansfield had exploded his bomb there was uncertainty as to the form a specification should take.[17] It had not merely to describe and define the invention with precision, it had to distinguish clearly what was new from what was old: not easy when describing a machine with 27 old elements and 13 new ones so interacting as to give a new and improved result.

Even though the essential requirements of a specification were vague, the problem of how to set one out had been exercising careful patentees even before Lord Mansfield's judgement. As is well known, James Watt had the advice of many friends in 1769 and finally prepared his specification on the lines suggested to him by Dr. Small. Aimé Argand, writing to Matthew Boulton in 1784 about his oil lamp patent which Boulton bought and had revoked (with accompanying financial loss), reported, 'I wrote my specification myself and made it as general and comprehensive as I could ... I consulted Mr. Fearn celebrated Advocate in Fetter Lane and very well acquainted with Specifications, our friend Mr. Moore ...',[18] that is, Samuel More, of the Society of Arts.[19]

Richard Arkwright, who learned to write late in life and always found it a great effort, had the specification of his spinning patent of 1769 prepared by a London attorney but for his second patent of 1775 he employed a local man. There can be little doubt that in this instance Arkwright intended that the specification should not fully and satisfactorily describe his alleged invention. The drawing was done by Charles Wilkinson, who kept an academy in Nottingham. Wilkinson also prepared the text of the specification in so far as it related directly to the figures in the drawing and the whole thing was put in more formal condition by William Crofts, clerk to a Nottingham attorney.[20] It was this specification that was the subject of three separate trials. Samuel More was a witness in two of them. Asked, in the witness box, if he could draw up a specification he replied 'I am continually drawing up specifications to machines. There is seldom a day when machines don't come before me and I draw up a specification for them.'[21] On another occasion he said 'No man in the United Kingdom is so often consulted upon patents as I am who gets nothing by it'.[22] So, among the assortment of people engaged in consultations on patent specifications and in drawing them up is the Secretary of a Society which from time to time emitted utterances that have been regarded an antipathetic to patents. This ought not to occasion surprise for, apart from the obvious liberty of the Secretary as a private person to hold opinions at variance with some official pronouncements,[23] by reason of its democratic nature and the breadth of opinion of its membership the Society was never set in the rigid anti-patent stance that some later spokesmen appeared to assume.[24]

Samuel More died in 1799 leaving the Society with the impossible task of appointing a successor to match the authority he had given the post. A most likely candidate and one who received much encouragement from members of the Society was Dr. Edmund Cartwright,[25] a man with eleven patents to his credit at that time, with more to follow. Cartwright would probably have been a most worthy successor to Samuel More had he not stood down in favour of Dr. Charles Taylor, who was probably the best known and best informed industrial chemist of the period. Taylor was an inventor and patentee and was much consulted on patent matters. On behalf of a group he referred to as 'Gentlemen of the County of York' he organized opposition to a patent for printing on woollens,[26] and according to some sources it was he who worked up the case against Arkwright on behalf of Lancashire cotton spinners which resulted in the revocation of Arkwright's second patent.[27] Nearly three years after accepting the Secretaryship of the Society of Arts he was a witness in a major patent trial relating to textile bleaching.[28]

Taylor was succeeded in 1817 by Arthur Aikin, who told the Society when he was interviewed for the post of Secretary that he was at that time occupied in drawing up patents and advising on scientific matters. But for this statement recorded by one of the Society's historians,[29] the full nature of Aikin's work in relation to patents could have been overlooked in the catalogue of activities of this many-sided man. If Aikin had not moved to the Society patents could well have become a primary activity, for with the death of William Nicholson (a chemist and patent practitioner of whom more will be said) only about eighteen months before that of Charles Taylor a slot was left open that none was so well-fitted to enter as Arthur Aikin. In 1815 there were far fewer chemical patents than mechanical[30] (the ratio was probably about one to ten) but there were proportionately fewer people possessed of some patent expertise who were competent to pursue this line of activity. As it was, throughout the period of his Secretaryship, Arthur Aikin may well have been the leading person to be consulted on chemical patents and for the drawing up of chemical specifications. He was called upon to be a witness in several patent actions and in 1829 gave evidence before a House of Commons Select

Committee on patents.[31] Soon after taking office with the Society he was co-patentee with James Jacks regarding an invention for preventing mildew in sailcloth.[32] An accomplished chemist, he was one of the founders of the Chemical Society which was inaugurated at a meeting in the Society's house in 1841 with Aikin as Treasurer, from which office he soon moved to become President.[33]

Notes and References to Part (i)

1 *Report from the Select Committee on the Law Relative to Patents for Inventions*, Ordered by The House of Commons to be printed, 12th June 1829 (hereafter referred to as '1829 Committee'); evidence of John Farey, p.18, 'When the King is indisposed, the patents are delayed at the stage when his signature is required'; p.19, 'During the late King's indispositions no patents were granted for many weeks together'; evidence of W.H. Wyatt, p.105, 'I have known patents to be delayed several months waiting for His Majesty's signature' ... which he is called upon twice to do in every patent'. 'The number of stages that each patent application in England had to go through necessitated constant attention in order that the documents might be issued as soon as received at the respective Government Offices, and I have known two or three of us from Fleet Street being sent to the Home Office daily, and sometimes without success for a week, but as the despatch boxes were always in anticipation of arrival it was necessary to be on the spot awaiting them.' Henry Gardner, Vice-President of the Society of Patent Agents, recalling 'Past Practice' in a paper read before that Society on 9th May 1894. A.A. Gomme, 'Patent Practice in the 18th Century: The Diary of Samuel Taylor, Threadmaker and Inventor, 1722–1723', *Transactions of the Newcomen Society*, Vol.XV, 1934–35, pp.209–24.

2 A.A. Gomme, *Patents of Invention*. 1946, The British Council, p.44.

3 John Davies, *A Collection of the Most Import Cases respective of Inventions*, 1816.

4 1829 Committee, *op.cit.*; evidence of John Farey, p.16. 'Of all the attornies I know, Mr. Abbott, of the Petty Bag Office, has done the greatest number; and of the patent agents, Mr. Moses Poole, of Lincoln's Inn, has passed the greatest number; p.17, 'Mr. Poole holds some office by which all patents must pass through his hands in one of their stages ... he passes a greater number of patents than any other person ... I have found that he obtains patents more expeditiously than some others'.

5 1829 Committee, *op.cit.*, evidence of Moses Poole, p.85. 'I have a written appointment from the Attorney General; Sir Samuel

Shepherd gave it me when my father died, who was in the office for thirty-six years before that period'.

[6] 1829 Committee, Moses Poole, *ibid.*, p.83.

[7] 1829 Committee, *op.cit.*, evidence of Francis Abbott, p.63.

[8] 1829 Committee, *op.cit.*, p.75.

[9] A.A. Gomme, *Patents of Invention, op.cit.*,p.34.

[10] Ibid.

[11] Ibid.

[12] James Puckle, *Portable Gun*, patent number 418 in printed series.

[13] James Puckle, *England's Interests, or a Brief Discourse of the Royal Fishery in a Letter to a Friend,* 1696 ed., pamphlet (British Library).

[14] Patent granted to John Liardet, 3rd April 1773, number 1040 in printed series.

[15] *Liardet v. Johnson,* 1778; see e.g. William Carpmael, *Law Reports of Patent Cases,* 1843, Vol.1, pp.36–7; Thomas Webster, *Reports on Letters Patent,* 1844, Vol.1, Pt.1, pp.53–4.

[16] Alistair J. Rowan, 'William Adam and Company', *Jnl.RSA*, Vol.CXXII (1973-4) pp.668 and 678.

[17] This was apparent in much evidence to the 1829 Committee. It was only with the rise of a specialist profession – that of patent agent – which understood the requirements of the Courts and was competent to adapt to these requirements as they evolved that a satisfactory degree of certainty could be achieved.

[18] Eric Robinson, 'James Watt and the Law of Patent', *Technology and Culture* (1971), pp.115–39, particularly at p.121.

[19] G.E. Mercer, 'Mr. More of the Adelphi', *Jnl.RSA*, Vol.CXLVII (1978–9), pp.96–103, 173–9 and 237–44; see especially pp.175 and 179.

[20] *Richard Arkwright v. Peter Nightingale*, Court of Common Pleas, 17th February 1785, 'copy from Mr. Gurney's shorthand notes'; John Rylands Library, Manchester, R13180. See also, John Davies, *op.cit.*

[21] *The Trial of a Cause ... to repeal a Patent ... granted to Mr. Richard Arkwright ... At Westminster-Hall, On Saturday the 25th of June, 1785.*

[22] *Richard Arkwright v. Peter Nightingale, op.cit.*

[23] G.E. Mercer, *op.cit.*, p.179.

[24] For example, 'During a period of our social history when protection and monopoly were held ... to be the very tap roots of commercial prosperity and manufacturing industry, the Society of Arts discountenanced patents and monopolies of every kind' – the Chairman of Council opening the 102nd Session, *Jnl.SA.*, Vol.IV (1855-6), 23rd Nov. 1855.

[25] H.T. Wood, *A History of the Royal Society of Arts,* 1913, p.334; *A Memoir of Edmund Cartwright* (M. Strickland presumed author), 1843, reprinted 1971, pp.162–72.

[26] Charles Taylor, Abstract of Documents – 1799, RSA, LA B9/36.

[27] R.S. Fitton and A.P. Wadsworth, *The Strutts and the Arkwrights, 1758–1830*, 1958, p.86. fn.5.

[28] *Tennant and ors. v. Slater and ors.*, 1802, John Davies, *op.cit.;* A.E.

Musson and Eric Robinson, *Science and Technology in the Industrial Revolution*, 1969, pp.289 and 322.

[29] H.T. Wood, *op.cit.,* p.336.

[30] 1829 Committee, p.75, evidence of William Newton, 'There is not, on an average, above one patent in a year for a medicine and perhaps not above one or two for dyeing, and those are nearly all the chemical patents that are taken'.

[31] 1829 Committee, pp.40--46.

[32] Patent granted to James Jacks of Camberwell and Arthur Aikin of the Adelphi, 11th May 1820, for *Method of preventing Mildew in Sail Cloth and other Canvas, and in other Manufacture made of Vegetable Fibre*, number 4456 in printed series.

[33] Betsy Rogers, *Georgian Chronicle: Mrs. Barbauld and her Family*, 1958, p.191; H.T. Wood, *op.cit.,* p.336; *DNB*.

Part (ii) Advisers, Specifiers and Publishers

The Secretary of the Society of Arts, Samuel More, gave evidence on behalf of the patentee at the trial in Westminster Hall on Saturday 25th June 1785 that resulted in Richard Arkwright's second patent for spinning machinery being revoked. A witness for those opposing the patent was Samuel Ewer, who described himself simply as 'Chairman of the Committee of Mechanics at the Adelphi'.[1] This was his qualification to speak on matters before the Court and it says much for the estimation in which the Society was held and of the respect with which the office of committee chairman was regarded that this brief statement was accepted as indicating the good standing of the witness. Commercial use was made of the regard in which the Society and its officers were held when a monthly publication, *The Technical Repository; containing Practical Information on Discoveries and Improvements in the Useful Arts,* was launched in 1822 under the editorship of Thomas Gill, 'A Chairman of the Committee of Mechanics in the Society for the Encouragement of Arts, Manufactures, and Commerce, Adelphi'.[2] The 'Prospectus of the Work' stated: 'The Proprietors have continually witnessed the ardent zeal with which Mr. Gill, for a long series of years, has fulfilled the duties attached to the important office of Chairman of the Committee of Mechanics, in that patriotic Institution, "The Society for the Encouragement of Arts, Manufactures, and Commerce", – incited solely by his desire to benefit society, through the powerful instrumentality of the resources and influence possessed by that Respectable Body: and had often thought, that, could he be induced to devote his attention to the conducting of a Practical Work of this description, no one would be more fitted to undertake the important task'. The proprietors went on to say that Mr. Gill 'is favoured with an extensive Correspondence with Foreigners of eminence in several walks of Science'. *Gill's Repository*, as it was soon known, provided information about patents and patented inventions interspersed with extracts from the Society's *Transactions* and material from foreign technical periodicals. In the first issue, Mr. Gill commended the Society: 'The Communications are many ... particularly in that of Mechanics: insomuch, that that Committee has been under the necessity of sitting in two evenings of every week ... and, in fact, it now affords one of the best opportunities of acquiring practical information that can be met with. Its meetings, therefore, are very fully attended by the Members of the Society, and also by their friends, who, under proper regulations, have the permission of being introduced'.[3]

Thomas Gill, eldest son of a Birmingham manufacturer of that name, had moved to London about 1800. In 1803 he contributed chapters on mill work and gearing for a revised edition of Imison's popular and respected *Elements of Science and Art*. In February of the same year he became a member of the Society of Arts, and a year later was elected a Chairman of the Committee of Mechanics. He remained in that office until 1826, when he was replaced by Timothy Bramah.[4] Before moving to London Gill had trained as a wheelwright and engineer, had assisted in the production of cotton spinning machinery for David Dale's New Lanark mills and had made improvements on the centrifugal governor.[5] Perhaps on the basis of experience gained when his father's patent of 1800 for rifling guns was obtained, he assisted Nicholas Paul of Geneva with his patent of 1802. Gill stated in *The Technical Repository* that he was 'appointed by Mr. Paul his patent agent'.[6] In 1834, from his 'Patent Agency and Consultation Office, No.125, Strand', he offered his services 'for settling specifications' and mentioned his 'capability of affording inventors that information as to the novelty and probable utility of their inventions, which may either lead them to secure their benefits to themselves by patenting them; or, on the other hand, to avoid the great expenses thereof'. He also described himself as a

'Specifier'.[7] It was essential that 'specifiers' and advisors of would-be patentees should be well acquainted with the current state of technical knowledge and be aware of prior inventions. In the absence of official publications on patents and with obstacles placed in the way of copying enrolled specifications, access to information on technical improvements was limited and the Society's committees must have been a most valuable source of information.

For many years Thomas Gill's co-chairman of the Committee of Mechanics was Bryan Donkin (1796–1855), whose name is familiar to students of the history of engineering and technology. Donkin had many inventions to his credit. He received Gold Medals of the Society for an instrument to measure the speed of rotation of machine parts and for a counting engine. He took out a patent with Henry Maudslay for epicycloids gears; was associated with William Congreve (inventor of the military rocket) in a method of printing stamps designed to reduce forgeries; introduced the preservation of food by canning; and made improvements in printing machinery. His greatest claim to fame lay in his making the paper-making machine – generally known as the 'Fourdrinier' – work. (Anyone acquainted with inventions knows that invention is only the beginning of a long expensive process; more inventions fail because they cannot be made to work in commercial practice than succeed.) A Vice-President of the Society of Arts, Donkin was also a Vice-President of the Institution of Civil Engineers of which he was a founder member.[8] As with Arthur Aikin, Donkin's genius was displayed in so many directions that his activities as a patent consultant and drafter of specifications seem not to have received the notice of historians.

Another engineer with so much to his credit that his patent activities seem to have been overlooked was John Millington (1779–1868). To Millington goes the credit of being invited to the first chair of engineering in England.[9] His books on engineering are among the earliest of their kind.[10] His initial training was in medicine and he was on the teaching staff of Guy's Hospital whilst practising as a civil engineer. For a time he was County Surveyor to Bedfordshire and he also served as engineer to a South London water undertaking. Shortly before leaving this country for South America in 1829 he was appointed engineer in charge of the erection of a bridge over the Thames at Marlow though the constructional work had barely begun when he left.[11] After giving lectures for two years at the Royal Institution, London, he was appointed Professor of Mechanics there in 1817. He participated (as did Bryan Donkin) in the establishment of the London Mechanics Institution – in which a leading role was played by the Fleet Street patent agent, J.C. Robertson – and was a Vice-President from its foundation.[12] He was a founding Fellow of the Royal Astronomical Society and served as its Secretary for some years.[13] His membership of the Society of Arts extended over nearly a quarter of a century, from 1803 to shortly before his departure for America.

Millington anticipated by twenty years the practical screw propulsion of ships as is evidenced by a patent granted in 1816.[14] Early in that year he was an expert witness in a major patent trial along with several prominent engineers including two other known specification drafters. John Farey and John Isaac Hawkins.[15] When giving evidence in 1829 before the Commons Select Committee on Patents he stated that he had 'acted for many years as an agent in obtaining patents as well as in drawing up specifications' and went on to speak of his experience in taking out foreign patents: 'Having been employed to obtain French patents, I have their code of laws at home at length, as well as those of most other countries'. He had an agent in France.[16]

Another engineer/specification drafter who displayed a considerable knowledge of foreign patent practice when giving evidence before the 1829 Committee was John Farey (1791–1851), whose connection with the Society of Arts could be said to span his life. At the close of his life he was a member of the Society's 1850 Committee on the Rights of Inventors, while not long after his birth his father was engaged in 'Experiments in the Growth of Timber Trees' under the stimulus of the Society, for which he received the Society's Silver Medal in 1805. The experiments 'had begun in 1794 with the approbation of the Duke of Bedford to whom the plantations belonged'.[17] John Farey Senior was agent to the Duke of Bedford and young John was brought up and educated at Woburn. John Farey Senior wrote extensively on agricultural

No. 5, DOUGHTY STREET, GRAY'S INN LANE,
London, 15th July, 1828.

A LIST

OF

THE CHARGES ORDINARILY MADE BY

MR. MILLINGTON,

Civil Engineer, and Surveyor of Manufactories and Machinery,

Professor of Mechanics in the Royal Institution of Great Britain, &c. &c.

TOGETHER WITH

AN ENUMERATION OF SOME OF THE PRINCIPAL OBJECTS TO WHICH HE DIRECTS HIS PROFESSIONAL ATTENTION.

VERBAL OPINION, or Advice respecting any object of Science, or Manufactures, 1 *Guinea.*

Written Opinion, or Report, in answer to any Case stated, according to its length, *from 2 to 5 Guineas.*

Making Working Drawings, such as Plans, Elevations, Sections, &c. of Mills, or Machinery, Locks, Docks, Basins, Bridges, Water Works, Gas Light Works, new Roads, Steam Engines, with or without Machinery attached to them, for Manufacturing or other Purposes; determining the Dimensions and Power of Machinery, and estimating the Price or Value of its Construction; and attending to the passing of Private Bills in Parliament, at the rate of 5 *Guineas per Diem upon the Time which shall be so occupied.*

[illegible]k's Time, so occupied, when Superintendance is necessary, at the rate of 1 *Guinea per Day*—When otherwise, [illegible]0s. 6d. *per Day.*

S[illegible]ations of Particulars for Work to form Contracts upon, 3s. 6d. *for each Common Law Sheet.*

[illegible]ance to arbitrate or settle Disputed [illegible] to sup[illegible]end the Construction of Millwright's Work—Buildings, or Machinery connected with Chemical or Mechanical [illegible]nufactures—to take Levels—to inspect or value Machinery or Premises already put up—to suggest Improvements or Alterations, or for the purpose of obtaining Information in order to give Evidence, or for other purposes—Conference with Counsel or Committees, at the rate of *Half a Guinea for each Hour which shall be so occupied, or* 5 *Guineas for the whole Day.* The Time necessary to go and return from such Business will be charged where the Distance exceeds One Mile from Home.

All Business in the Country at the rate of 5 *Guineas per Day* upon the Time occupied, as well on such Business, as in travelling, together with all Expenses out of pocket.

Attendance on any Court of Justice for the purpose of giving Evidence, or explaining Processes or Machinery, 5 *Guineas per Day*, exclusive of all Expences which may be incurred.

IN PATENT BUSINESS.

Drawing and Settling the Title of a Patent for an Invention, as a Ground for applying for the King's Royal Letters Patent, 1 *Guinea.*

Passing a Patent throughout the various Offices up to its receiving the Great Seal, 10 *Guineas.*

Drawing and Settling the Specification of a Letters Patent, at the rate of 1 *Guinea for every six common law sheets,* exclusive of making Drawings, and all attendance to receive Instructions, and to alter, amend, or improve the same when drawn, which will be charged at the be[illegible]-mentioned rate of 10s. 6d. *per Hour.*

Original Drawings of Patent or other Machinery at the rate of 5s. *per Hour* upon the Time they occupy. Copies of them 2s. 6d. *per Hour,* exclusive of vellum, parchment, or paper.

Obtaining a Foreign Patent, 5 *Guineas,* exclusive of all Postage and Expences.

Models of Machines, &c. also made from description or otherwise, and charged on the lowest Terms, according to the Time they occupy the Workmen.

Instructions given in the various Branches of Science, and original, or other Experiments tried or repeated, at the rate of 10s. 6d. *per Hour* upon the whole Time of their preparation, exclusive of all Expense for Materials, Breakage, &c.

Land Surveying and Mapping in all its Branches, and Artificer's Work measured and valued at the usual rates of Charge.

Business requiring a considerable extension of Time, will only be done on lower Terms by Special Agreement with the Parties.

Orders for Steam Engines and extensive Machinery executed with the First Houses in the Country on Commission.—And Country Business executed in London, in the same manner.

N.B. MR. MILLINGTON *has established a correspondence with the principal Cities of Europe and America, and the East Indies, for Foreign Patents, and other Business.*

Fees of a patent practitioner of the 1820s. John Millington's correspondence concerning a bridge at Marlow included a letter written on the back of a fee-sheet relating to his civil engineering and patent activities. (Reproduced by permission of the Buckinghamshire Record Office) and geological matters[18] and his children showed early literary and technical ability. Young John was only a few years behind his father in receiving a Silver Medal of the Society.[19] This was for an instrument for making perspective drawings, one of many improvements in drawing instruments he devised. While still only in his early twenties he received the Society's Gold Medal for a machine for drawing ellipses. He had prepared drawings for *Rees' Cyclopaedia, The Edinburgh Encyclopaedia* and corresponding publications with a technical content from the age of fourteen and also at an early age made drawings for engraving by Wilson Lowry for the publication, under the authority of a group of leading civil engineers, of Smeaton's Reports and Drawings. Some of the illustrations in Vols.XXVI (1808) to XXXI (1813) of the *Transactions of the Society of Arts* are by him.[20] From about 1810 he was drafting patent specifications[21] and around 1815 was witness in a patent trial of Heathcoat's. This was possibly the first of many patent trials at which he appeared as an expert witness. Probably no one attended as many such trials as expert witness between 1815 and 1840 as John Farey.[22]

The obituary notice of Farey in the *Proceedings of the Institution of Civil Engineers*[23] has a charming passage referring to his qualities as an expert witness and to the character of his principal assistant: 'His laborious research into authority for cases was proverbial, and his habits of order and regularity rendered his office and library models of these qualities. In this, as in the preparation of drawings for specifications, he received invaluable assistance from Mrs. Farey, a lady of rare attainments, who to great amiability of disposition, and a thorough knowledge of the duties of her sex, joined almost masculine scientific attainments, which she employed as modestly as profitably, in aiding the labours of her husband'.

It was not only a wife of amiable disposition who enabled John Farey to get through a prodigious amount of work; the Farey business was very much a family concern. When John went to Russia in 1819 to assist in establishing an ironworks, patent matters were probably left in charge of his younger brother Joseph. (Joseph twice received Silver Palettes of the Society for machine drawings.[24]) Certainly when John went to Devon in 1821 to work full time with Heathcoat he relinquished the consultancy and patent business in Joseph's favour. However, a variety of domestic troubles caused John to return to London and patents in 1826.

Joseph was not the only member of the family associated with patent work. A notebook belonging to Henry Farey (younger than John by nine years) came to light some years ago[25] and from this we know that Henry and his two sisters helped with patent drawings and other activities of their eldest brother. The first entry in the notebook is dated for 1st January 1819 and reads, 'Began shading parchment copy of Clegg's patent gazometer. Sophia made the copy.'[26] Henry's drawing would be that required for enrolment at the Rolls Chapel or other enrolment office, while Sophia's would be an identical copy on paper for retention by the patentee after certification by the enrolment office.

When giving evidence to the 1829 Commons Select Committee, Farey spoke at some length about the introduction of a textile machine and remarked, 'I prepared the specification for Mr. Dyer's patent, in conjunction with Mr. Nicholson, in 1812'. [27] It is likely that Farey acquired his earliest patent experience with William Nicholson, who must surely rank among the earliest to practise the skills now regarded as the particular business of a patent agent. He may have been active in this line as early as 1790.[28] A patent of 1777 seems to have been taken out by him[29] and in 1790 he patented a significant invention in printing.[30] In 1807 he was consulted as patent agent by König, who was developing his cylinder printing press for newspapers.[31] Nicholson was a witness in the Boulton and Watt action against Jabez Hornblower in 1796[32] and in 1802 drew up a specification which featured in an unusual action in the courts.[33] Between these and numerous other activities he planned waterworks for West Middlesex and Portsmouth.[34] Nicholson did not become a member of the Society of Arts until December 1799. This was two months after the death of Samuel More, with whom he seems to have been acquainted, for when the post of Assistant Secretary to the Society was to be filled in 1798 More 'received a warm recommendation of Taylor's candidacy from William Nicholson, chemist, patent agent and inventor'.[35] (This candidate was Thomas – 'Platonist' – Taylor who served the Society for many years.)

William Nicholson (1753–1815) was the son of a solicitor. At the age of sixteen he entered the East India Company's service. For a time, from about 1776, he was Wedgwood's commercial agent in Europe. He had many inventions and technical discoveries to his credit and read papers before the Royal Society on chemical and electrical subjects,[36] but it was probably by his work as a publisher that he made his greatest contribution to the development of science. In referring to Nicholson as a witness at the Hornblower trial, James Watt, Junior, described him as 'Mr. Nicholson author of the *Chemical Dictionary*'.[37] The *Dictionary* was published in 1795 and in 1797 Nicholson brought out *A Journal of Natural Philosophy, Chemistry and the Arts*. This is regarded as the first general scientific periodical in England published independently of the academies or learned societies[38] and was a great success soon to be emulated by others.

Nicholson's Journal soon became an important vehicle for the communication of original scientific papers but technical consultancy, preparation of patent specifications and the publication of a periodical devoted to scientific and/or technical matters were common features of the professional activities of many specification drafters who followed Nicholson. Usually these periodicals had a practical bias and provided information about recently granted patents. The first publication of this nature to be produced over a sustained period antedated *Nicholson's Journal* by a few years; this was *The Repertory of Arts and Manufactures*, published by Paternoster Row booksellers G. & T. Wilkie in 1794 but acquired a few years later by Walter Henry Wyatt, who was a Life Member of the Society of Arts by 1820. Wyatt seems to have included the processing of patent applications and/or specifications among his activities.[39] *The Repertory* continued to circulate until 1862 when it had for some years been in the hands of Messrs. Carpmael & Co., patent agents.[40] In 1820 *The London Journal of Arts and Sciences* appeared, soon to be popularly known simply as *Newton's London Journal; Gill's Repository* came out in 1822 and *The Mechanics' Magazine* edited by J.C. Robertson, Fleet Street patent agent, first appeared in the latter part of August 1823. Within a couple of months the *Register of the Arts and Sciences, Improvements and Discoveries* was available. This was published by George Hebert of Cheapside and again gave information on Society of Arts' premiums as well as on patents. The *Register* changed its style, title and editor for a New Series that began on 1st March 1827 as *The Register of Arts and Journal of Patent Inventions* under Luke Hebert, 'Mechanical Draftsman and Civil Engineer', who enlarged on this occupational style in his first Preface in the announcement, 'The Editor being professionally a Mechanical Draftsman and Patent Agent ...'. Other periodicals followed; every patent agency worth its salt seemed to find it desirable by the 1840s to seek a little profit and advertisement by publishing a technical journal or handbook of patent information.[41]

The London Journal merits particular mention: It was established at the initiative of a London publisher, Sherwood, who prevailed upon William Newton (1796–1861) to edit the new periodical. Newton came of a family of land surveyors and draughtsmen which had long included the preparation of maps and the production of globes among its activities at 'Ye Globe and Sun, Chancery Lane, Fleet Street'. William Newton's 'talent as a mechanical draughtsman was early recognized by his appointment to the profitable post of draughtsman to the several offices in which the specifications of patents were recorded'.[42] Not later than 1819, Newton turned his hand to preparing specifications and applying for patents on behalf of clients. He soon built up a thriving practice with considerable overseas connections. In the region of two hundred patents were taken out in his name or the names of his sons by 1852,[43] exceeding even those in the name of Moses Poole. (It was not uncommon in this period for an agent to take out patents for clients in his own name and then to assign the rights after grant.) In 1861, Newton's *Memoir*-writer referred to patent agency as 'a professional branch which he may be said to have created'.[44] What has gone before in this paper shows this to have been a munificent tribute but those generous words indicate not only Newton's standing among his fellows but the view that in him the profession was seen to have come of age. The writer of the *Memoir* went on to record: 'The difficulties of performing the duties of editor (of *The London Journal of Arts*) were, from the regulations of the Enrolment Offices, very great, but for some years they were satisfactorily combated. The annually increasing number of Patents eventually, however, made it impossible to do more than to record the titles of all the Patents.'

The passing of the Patent Law Amendment Act in 1852 did away with the enrolment offices with their restrictive regulations and established a single Patent Office to receive applications for patents and for the filing and publishing of specifications and other matters relating to patents. Early in 1853, William Marwick Michell, then employed by Messrs. Newton and Son, where he worked on the *London Journal*, accepted an invitation to join the publishing branch of the new Patent Office. 'During the previous thirteen years [viz., from 1840 to 1853] he had been engaged in the editorship of two scientific periodicals, principally devoted to the publication of abridgements of specifications, notices of new inventions, and other matters of interest to inventors and patentees. Throughout that period he had also been constanly occupied in the various duties pertaining to a patent agent's office, more especially in making extensive searches to determine the novelty of inventions, preparing analytical indexes of patented inventions, advising inventors, drawing up specifications, etc., etc. At the Patent Office Michell soon produced the first official periodical directed specifically to providing information about patents,[45] Issue No. 1 of *The Commissioners of Patents' Journal* appeared on 7th January 1854 to start an unbroken series of which the present title is *The Official Journal (Patents).*

Notes and References to Part (ii)

1 *The Trial of a Cause ... to repeal a Patent ... granted to Mr. Richard Arkwright.*
2 The Technical Repository, Vol.1 (1822). The room in the house of the Society of Arts in which were displayed for public examination models and devices which had been the subjects of awards was known as 'The Repository'.
3 Ibid., p.76.
4 R.W. Allott, 'Joseph Bramah and his Family as Members of the Society, 1783–1845'. *Jnl.RSA.*, Vol.CVIII (1959–60), p.64.
5 Thomas Gill, *Gill's Machinery Improved*, 1839.
6 *The Technical Repository, op.cit.*, p.B2.
7 *Gill's Machinery Improved, op.cit.*, title page.

[8] *Dictionary of National Biography.* See also W.H.G. Armytage, *A Social History of Engineering*, 1961, pp.107, 122 and 128.

[9] Negley Harte and John North, *The World of University College London 1828–1978*, p.57. Unpublished, typescript at UCL, 'History of the Faculty of Engineering', pp.2–4.

[10] John Millington, *An Epitome of ... Natural and Experimental Philosophy,* 1823; *An Epitome of ... Mechanical Philosophy,* 1830; *Elements of Civil Engineering*, Philadelphia, 1839. The 1823 edition was translated into German and published from Vienna in 1825; the present author is indebted to Mr. Stephen Buckland for drawing this to his notice.

[11] Charles Stewart Drewry, *A Memoir on Suspension Bridges*, 1832, pp.144–6; p.146, 'The erection of the bridge was then placed in the hands of Mr. Tierney Clark, the engineer of the Hammersmith Bridge. The bridge now erecting at Marlow, under his direction, is totally different from Professor Millington's design.'

[12] *The Mechanics Magazine,* 15th Nov. 1823, Vol.1, p.177; 'Public Meeting for the establishment of The London Mechanics' Institute' – letters from Lord Brougham, Professor Millington, Jeremy Bentham and others read. C.D. Burns, *A Short History of Birkbeck College (University of London),* 1924, p.29, 'The Institution opened on 20 February, 1824 ... with an inaugural address by Dr. Birkbeck and a lecture by Professor Millington'.

[13] *DNB.*

[14] Patent granted on 31st July, number 3977 in printed series.

[15] John Davies, *A Collection of the Most Important Cases, 1816, Bovill v. Moore,* pp.361–414, more particularly at pp.407, 408 and 410.

[16] 1829 Committee, pp.98 and 99.

[17] *Trans. S. of A.*, Vol.XXIII, (1805), p.112 *et seqq.*

[18] John Farey's *General View of the Agriculture and Minerals of Derbyshire*, 1811, enjoyed a considerable reputation.

[19] *Trans. S. of A.*, Vol.XXXII (1814), pp.23 and 71. See also Vol.XXXIII (1815), p.69.

[20] H.T. Wood, *A History of the Royal Society of Arts*, 1913, p.177.

[21] In a letter written c.1814 to the editor of *The Encyclopaedia Britannica*, Farey said that he had been employed in investigating technical history and drawing up patent specifications for the past four or five years. The present author is indebted to Mr. A.P. Woolrich of Bridgwater for this information.

[22] This opinion is arrived at from an examination of trials reported in *Law Reports of Patent Cases,* William Carpmael, 1843.

[23] *Proc.Inst. Civil Engineers*, Vol.XI (1851), pp.100–102.

[24] H.T. Wood, *op.cit.*

[25] *'The Farey Diary', 1819,* Trans. Newcomen Society, Vol.XVII (1936–7), pp.215–18.

[26] Patent granted on 24th July 1818 to Samuel Clegg, number 4283 in printed series, for an Improved Gazometer or Gasholder. The specification was enrolled on 8th Jan, 1819. Clegg received the

Society's Silver Medal in 1808 for a gas-holder (See Plate 17 in *The Royal Society of Arts 1754–1954*, Derek Hudson and Kenneth W. Luckhurst, 1954); this prize-winning form and not the patented gas-holder was a practical success.

[27] Joseph Chessborough Dyer, patent of 30th Oct, 1811, numbered 3862 in printed series, *Machinery to be used and applied in Manufacturing Cards for Carding Wool,* etc.

[28] *DNB.*

[29] Patent of 14th July 1777, number 1159 in printed series, *Securing the Property of Persons purchasing Shares of State-lottery Tickets*; a curious patent in view of the credit given to John Molesworth, mathematician, for an invention in this field for which a patent was granted to Molesworth only two months later, cf. 1170 of 1777 and p.27 of the official catalogue to *A Gallery of Portraits of Inventors*, etc., 1856.

[30] Patent of 29th April 1790, number 1748 in printed series.

[31] *DNB.*

[32] Eric Robinson, 'James Watt and the Law of Patents', *Technology and Culture* (1971), pp.115–39, more particularly at p.157, James Watt Junior quoted, 'Mr. Davies Gilbert and Mr. William Nicholson author of the Chemical Dictionary, their whole evidence going merely to the insufficiency of the specification ...'.

[33] John Davies, *op.cit.,* p.229, *Smith v. Dickenson,* John Farey's report of this action in 1829 Committee, App.B, p.194, refers to a meeting of the parties with 'Mr. Nicholson, who was employed to draw the specification'. Davies reports that 'Mr. N' and Mr. F' were at the meeting; it is unlikely that the eleven-year old John Farey Junior was at the meeting. Did John Farey Senior dabble in patents?

[34] *DNB.*

[35] L.S. Boas, 'Thomas Taylor, Platonist (1758–1835), at the Society of Arts'. *Jnl.RSA*, Vol.CXV (1966–7), p.743.

[36] *DNB.*

[37] Eric Robinson, *op.cit.*

[38] S. Lilley, 'Nicholson's Journal' (1797–1813), *Annals of Science*, Vol.VI (1950), pp.78–101, more particularly at p.80.

[39] 1829 Committee. This observation is based on W.H. Wyatt's evidence, pp.103–6, more especially pp.104, ll.56 and 57.

[40] Henry Gardner, *Past Practice* (see Part I), pp.5 and 6.

[41] Ibid.

[42] Memoir of William Newton, *Proc. Inst. Civil Engineers*, Vol.21 (1861–2), pp.592–3.

[43] Bennet Woodcroft, *Alphabetical Index of Patentees of Inventions*, officially published 1854, commercially reprinted 1969.

[44] Memoir of William Newton, *op.cit.* Against the prominent standing held by the Newtons as patent agents should be placed their continuing business as manufacturers and vendors of globes and optical instruments. At the 1851 Exhibition, 'Wm. Newton & Son, Manufacturers' displayed a variety of terrestrial and celestrial

globes, orreries and a sun dial, while W.E. & F. Newton of the same address–'3 Fleet-street, Temple-bar and 66 Chancery-lane (Manufactory)'–advertised themselves in the Official Catalogue as globe manufacturers to Her Majesty and vendors of telescopes, medical and other microscopes, opera glasses, magic lanterns and dissolving view apparatus. For most, if not all, of those who practised as patent agents in 1851 and for many years to follow patents formed only a part of business activities.

[45] Obituary Notice, William Marwick Michell, *The Engineer*, Vol.59 (1885), p.238. Quotation extracted from unpublished official report on Patent Office. In 1872 a young man working with Michell at the Patent Office left to edit the *Journal of the Society of Arts* and later to become the Society's Secretary; this was Henry Trueman Wood.

Part (iii) Men of Law

The readiness with which the chemists and engineers mentioned earlier in this study as drafters of patent specifications turned to publishing and lecturing indicates a valuable combination of qualities. A facility for written and oral communication is not universal even today among technical people and was less common 150 years ago (George Stephenson's way could have been smoother if he had been able to communicate more lucidly with non-technical men) and such a facility was as essential for the specification drafters of the early nineteenth century as it is for the modern patent agent, for he must be able to convey technical concepts in a manner that is not only technically accurate but which will have clarity and precision when considered by lawyers. Careful use of words is a prerequisite for lawyers and they start with an advantage in preparing a patent specification so long as the invention they have to describe lies within their technical competence. The Mr. Rotch that Moses Poole recommended to his clients[1] was a barrister who, during the 1820s at least, turned his hand to drawing up specifications.[2] It will be recalled that Aimé Argand consulted 'Mr. Fearn celebrated Advocate in Fetter Lane and very well acquainted with the Specifications and the Philosophical Subjects of them'[3] and it is reasonable to assume that prudent inventors advised by equally prudent attornies or solicitors had specifications settled by counsel. However, Mr. Rotch was not recommended by Moses Poole for the settling of a document drawn by someone else but as a 'specifier' or specification drafter in the manner of Farey, Millington and Gill.

Benjamin Rotch (1794–1854), second son of Benjamin Rotch of Castle Hall, near Milford Haven, was admitted a member of

Lincoln's Inn in 1816 and Clarke's New Law List for 1820 describes him as 'Special pleader and conveyancer, 15 South Moulton Street'. About this time he began to practice in the Northern Circuit, travelling the Yorkshire West Riding and Liverpool Sessions where patent cases were not unknown. Later he was Chairman of Middlesex Quarter Sessions and sat as Member for Knaresborough for three years (1832–5).[4] Elected a member of the Society of Arts in 1820, he displayed a very lively interest in its affairs for more than thirty years and was appointed a Vice-President in 1848. He provided the Society with descriptions of several of his miscellaneous innovations and presented for display in the Society's Model Room or museum his 'Feeding Syphon for the Sick Room' – 'Though apparently a trifling invention, its importance and comfort will be fully appreciated in the chamber of the invalid'.[5] In 1821 he received a Silver Medal of the Society for an instrument which he called 'An Arcograph, or Instrument for Drawing and Measuring Arcs of Large Circles'.[6] The essential element in this invention lay in the addition of a graduated quadrant to an instrument used by mechanical draughtsmen and developed by John Farey and Peter Nicholson (both of whom received Silver Medals of the Society) a few years earlier. Rotch had four or five patents in his name[7] with titles that do not strike a modern reader as representing inventions of great significance but – as with his feeding siphon – though the inventions may seem trifling their importance was appreciated by those directly involved. His 'Fid for the Upper Masts of Ships' (1822), 'By which Ships may strike their Topmasts or Topgallant Masts, at any moment in less than one minute', received 'strong approbation and patronage from those best qualified to appreciate its merits' and was 'considered to be of invaluable service in nautical operations'.[8] Rotch's fids had been employed on four Royal Navy ships within two years of the patent and early in 1825 when fitted to the 120-gun *Prince Regent* were demonstrated in the presence of Mr. Rotch (who inspected the workmanship, presumably by climbing the rigging), the captains of four ships of the line, representatives of the Lords of the Admiralty, and officers of Chatham dockyard.[9] Three years later, Luke Hebert's *Register of Arts* by way of preface to a description of another of Rotch's 'trifling inventions' observed, 'We have often remarked, that the mechanical inventions of the above-mentioned eminent barrister, are distinguished alike, by extraordinary simplicity in their construction, and great practical utility'.[10] Rotch's interest in the dissemination of technical knowledge is evidenced by his presence and support at the founding of the London Mechanics' Institution in 1823 and of the British Association in 1831.[11]

Until the beginning of the nineteenth century the obtaining of patents was primarily a part of the business of solicitors and, having obtained the patent grants, these solicitors often prepared specifications. With the rise of specialist specification drafters the bulk of the business moved into other hands but, nevertheless, of the 'Patent and Design Registration Agents; listed in the London Post Office Directories of the mid 1860s one in six indicated that they were also solicitors. The number of people operating in two professions concurrently gradually decreased and over the past fifty years very few indeed have practised as patent agent and solicitor simultaneously.[12] One of the people in the period covered by this study who combined both professions was John Bethell (1804–67), who is singled out for mention on account of his contributions to the Society's affairs. Like Benjamin Rotch, John Bethell was also an inventor in his own right[13] and his process for preserving timber by pressure impregnation with creosote provided a base for British and many foreign railway tracks for well over a century and by the time of his death, and despite a multitude of other activities, he had the management of several large creosoting and chemical works in England and abroad.

Rotch and Bethell were lawyers with a natural inclination towards mechanical matters. There were technically-trained people in their days as in ours with leanings towards law, and patent proceedings provided scope for their talents. As the number of patents sought and granted increased during the nineteenth century so did the amount of patent litigation, thereby providing openings for lawyers with technical propensities and also for some people for whom the law was not their earliest field of study. Benjamin Rotch, trained for the law from the first, acquired an extensive practice as a patent counsel. It may well be that he was the first specialist patent barrister.[14] As the amount of litigation increased he was, of course, joined by others whose briefs were primarily directed to patent matters, such as Richard Godson, a Wrangler whose *Practical Treatise on The Law of Patents for Inventions* (first edition 1823) was highly regarded, and by another Cambridge mathematician, Thomas Webster (1810–75). Webster, whose initial interests were technical, became Secretary to the Institution of Civil Engineers in 1837 and before and whilst holding that office he published works on the motion of fluids, hydrostatics and the principles of capillary attraction.[15] But he also read for the Bar. In 1839, William Henry Maule, a Senior Wrangler and a close friend of Charles Babbage in their Cambridge days, was promoted to the Bench as a Judge of Common Pleas and invited Webster to be his assistant.[16] Webster was called to the Bar in 1841 and in the same year published his *Law and Practice of Patents for Inventions*; other publications in this field followed.

Webster was one of the most significant recruits to the Society of Arts of the nineteenth century. His record of service has never been adequately recorded but it was great, as was that of his son Richard who, as Chairman of Council in 1890, referred to the numerous discussions on patent law that had taken place in the Society's house from 1850, saying, 'I have been present from my boyhood at many of these discussions ...'.[17] Of the many who campaigned for patent reform through the nineteenth century pride of place must be given to Thomas Webster, who laboured with tremendous persistence and patience for this cause through the Society of Arts, the British Association and other organizations.

For several years before Thomas Webster joined the Society, its membership and funds had been declining. The opening of the 1841–2 Session brought the disclosure that there was only £400 in hand and that that would soon be eaten up by essential routine expenses. Prospects for survival looked bleak. A committee was set up to consider the Society's condition, and Thomas Webster, a comparatively young man who had been a member of the Society for less than four years, was appointed Chairman. This crisis in the Society's affairs resulted in what was virtually a re-foundation. The most important reform suggested by Webster's committee was that a managing group or Council should be appointed to have full control of the Society's business. Other suggestions were that the principal object of the Wednesday evening meetings should be the reading and discussion of communications on the arts and manufactures of the country and that, because the exclusion of patented inventions from awards had been extremely detrimental to the interest of the Society, regulations disqualifying patented inventions should be rescinded. A Rule bearing on these disqualifications and which had been in force for three-quarters of a century was omitted from Volume LIV of the *Transactions* (1841–3)[18] and that volume carried an Appendix of papers 'read before the Society at their Wednesday evening meetings ... including those relating to *Patented Inventions*, which were, until very recently, entirely prohibited from being brought before the Society in any shape whatever'.[19] These included papers presented by Benjamin Rotch and John Bethell. In 1890, the Attorney-General, Sir Richard Webster, QC, shortly to become Lord Alverstone, LCJ and the Society's President, summed up succinctly the changes which had been initiated by his father and collaborators in 1841: 'In place of encouraging individuals, the Society has of late years assisted in the reform of the Patent-laws, which provide inventors with the protection they require'.[20] In the midst of the Society's 1841 crisis the Secretary, W.A. Graham, resigned and Thomas Webster undertook to find a replacement, which he did by prevailing upon Francis Whishaw – an engineer and patentee – to take on the duties. From Whishaw sprang the Great Exhibition of 1851 and much more. He seems to have been chosen to be the first curator of the Patent Museum in 1856 but died before taking up the appointment.[21] Whishaw continued the tradition – only briefly broken by Graham – which stretched from the eighteenth into the twentieth century of Secretaries of high technical attainments and with patent interests.

Led by Thomas Webster, Benjamin Rotch and John Bethell, a vigorous recruitment campaign was put under way. Almost the first to come in, proposed by John Bethell, were William Newton and his son, patent agents of Chancery Lane. Webster brought in William Carpmael, a civil engineer who had read for the Bar and become a patent agent. The list of engineers and patentees introduced to the Society in the next five or six years was extensive. Many made considerable contributions to the revitalization of the Society and several made outstanding contributions to the development of the patent system. Two particularly closely associated with the patent reform movement that led to the Patent Law Amendment Act of 1852 (drafted by Thomas Webster) were Richard Prosser, engineer and patentee of Birmingham, introduced by John Bethell, and Bennet Woodcroft, textile manufacturer, patentee and patent consultant of Manchester, introduced by Thomas Webster. Although Woodcroft has taken the main credits, the modern system of patent classification and of abridgments owes much to both, and when the Patent Office Library was opened in 1855 with the private libraries of these two men as its nucleus, Prosser's contribution was the greater.

There were, of course, others who helped in the salvation of the Society in the early 1840s but patent practitioners were among the leaders and it is not surprising that the Society was soon active for patent reform. The Act of 1852 was only a beginning and the Society's lecture hall witnessed many discussions during the remainder of the century, though none was so lively as the debates on the Patent Bills of the 1870s. Anyone who cares to follow in the Society's *Journal* the tremendous discussion opened in 1877 by Henry Trueman Wood, then Assistant Secretary, will see many familiar names of the profession of patent agent among the participants. Before the Institute of Patent Agents was founded what better place for patent agents to meet for open discussion than the Society of Arts?

Notes and References to Part (iii)

1 1829 Committee, p.83.
2 Ibid., p.88; the evidence of Joseph Merry on Rotch as a specification drafter is interesting.
3 Part (i) of this Study.
4 M. Stenton, *Who's Who of British Members of Parliament*, Vol.1, 1834–85; 1976.
5 *Trans. S. of A.*, Vol.LV (1845), pp.133–4.
6 *Gill's Technical Repository*, Vol.I, (1822), pp.260–61 and Plate XVI.
7 In printed series numbered 4839 (1823), 5474 (1827), 5922 (1830), 13231 (1850); 4025 (1816) may have been in his father's name.
8 *The Register of the Arts and Sciences*, Vol.II, (1825), pp.233–6.
9 Ibid.
10 *The Register of Arts*, New Series, Vol.I (1828), p.280, 30th Dec. 1827.

[11] *The Mechanics' Magazine* for Saturday 15th Nov. 1823 (Vol.1; p.177) reported on the meeting the previous Tuesday evening 'for the establishment of the London Mechanics' Institute' at which the first resolution on establishment was 'proposed by Mr. Sheriff Laurie and seconded by B. Rotch, barrister'. At the first meeting of The British Association for the Advancement of Science held at York in 1831 a Sub-Committee on the Mechanical Arts had B. Rotch as a member; *B.A. Reports*, Vol.I.

[12] Cf. Memoir of Montague Solomon (1866–1934), *Trans. Chartered Institute of Patent Agents*, Vol.LIII 91934–5), P.217; 'one of the very few men who combined the profession of a patent Agent with that of a solicitor and practised both professions concurrently until his death'.

[13] Printed series numbers of John Bethell's pre-1852 patents are 6599 (1834), 6757 (1835), 7731 (1838), 8456 (1840) and 12250 (1848); the 1838 patent was for 'Rendering wood etc. less pervious to water'. He took out eight more patents between 1853 and 1864. *The Mechanics; Magazine* for 8th March 1867, pp.142–3, carried a generous obituary notice which records a remarkable series of commercially practised inventions and heavy business commitments.

[14] This observation is based on a perusal of reported patent cases; although Benjamin Rotch was a counsel in, for example, merely a dozen reported cases for the years 1826–9 a minority of cases only is reported and in those the name Rotch appears more frequently than any other. Professor Eric Robinson in *James Watt and the Law of Patents (op.cit.)*, p.118, is of opinion that 'certain specialists in the patent law were beginning to emerge by the last quarter of the eighteenth century if not before', but it is not until the second quarter of the nineteenth century that lawyers who made patents their primary interest are noticed.

[15] Thomas Webster, *The Theory of Equilibrium and Motion of Fluids* (1836), *The Principles of Capillary Attraction* (1838), *The Principles of Hydrostatics* (1838); other technical publications were *The Port and Docks of Birkenhead* (1848) and republished *Reports of the Conservators of the Mersey, 1853 and 1857*.

[16] Bernard S. Becker, *Scientific London* (1874), p.111.

[17] *Jnl. RSA,* Vol.XXXIX (1890–91), Chairman's Opening Address at p.11.

[18] H.T. Wood, *A History of the Royal Society of Arts*, 1913, pp.345–51 and p.243.

[19] *Trans. S. of A.*, Vol.LIV (1841–3), p.155.

[20] *Jnl. S. of A.*, Vol.XXXIX, p.11, *op.cit.*

[21] Obituary Notice, Francis Whishaw, MInstCE, *The Civil Engineer and Architect's Journal,* 1856, p.365.

Index of Significant Names